GLENCOE
Backpack Reader

COURSE **1** BOOK **1**

WITH A
GRAPHIC NOVEL
IN EVERY UNIT!

www.glencoe.com

Glencoe

New York, New York   Columbus, Ohio   Chicago, Illinois   Peoria, Illinois   Woodland Hills, California

Acknowledgments

Grateful acknowledgment is given authors, publishers, photographers, museums, and agents for permission to reprint the following copyrighted material. Every effort has been made to determine copyright owners. In case of any omissions, the Publisher will be pleased to make suitable acknowledgments in future editions.
Acknowledgments continued on page R2.

The *McGraw-Hill* Companies

Send all inquiries to:
Glencoe/McGraw-Hill
8787 Orion Place
Columbus, OH 43240-4027
ISBN-13: 978-0-07-874332-0
ISBN-10: 0-07-874332-X
Printed in the United States of America.

6 7 8 9 110/055 10 09 08

Table of Contents

Table of Contents

UNIT 3 What's fair and what's not? _____ 140

Why read?

Where can you turn when you want to laugh, learn something new, or understand different cultures? What can make your imagination soar? Reading can do all of these things for you. The selections in this unit will provide you with many possible answers to the question: **Why read?**

Key Reading Skills

As you read the selections in this unit, apply these reading skills.

- **Identifying Main Idea and Supporting Details** Find the most important idea in a selection or part of a selection. Find the details that back up the main idea.
- **Setting a Purpose for Reading** Before reading a selection, think about what you'd like to get out of it.
- **Skimming and Scanning** *Skimming* is reading over a selection quickly to get a general idea of what it's about. *Scanning* is moving your eyes quickly through a selection to find specific information.
- **Understanding Graphics** Look at the drawings, pictures, maps, charts, photos, and graphs in a selection. These graphics will help you better understand the selection.

STAR SPOTLIGHT

Marc John Jefferies
—Interview by Gerri Miller

Why does a talented young actor find time for reading?

He's one of the busiest people in show biz—and he's only 15. Marc John Jefferies has already starred in hit movies like *Stuart Little 2*, *The Haunted Mansion*, and *Charlie's Angels: Full Throttle*. Marc has also created the Secret Agent MJJ book series for young adults. As if that weren't enough, Marc also likes to perform stand-up comedy in clubs in Los Angeles, California. Scholastic News Online recently caught up with Marc and asked him about his many projects. Here's what he had to say:

Want to be an actor? Marc says you must learn to read!

Q. Do you prefer drama or comedy?

Marc. I was the youngest kid to perform at The Laugh Factory, a comedy club in California, so I really like comedy because I guess I am naturally funny. Drama gives the skills in order to play different roles and to bring out emotion. I would have to say that I like to do both. There is no preferred role.

Q. Do you write your own comedy act?

Marc. I write it and my dad critiques it to make sure I don't go overboard. Eddie [Murphy] and I would do a little bit of his stand-up and he would tell me what to do and how I could change it to make it funnier. I actually lived with him for a while because his son, Miles, is my best friend.

Q. Describe your style of comedy.

Marc. I use real-life situations—things that I see each day and things people can relate to, things that happen to them. I make that funny and I use that in my comedy.

Q. Do you think you would like to do stand-up comedy as a job?

Marc. Yes, I really do like to do stand-up comedy. I like to warm up the crowd.

Q. Tell me about your book series. ❶

❶ Scanning
Why is Marc writing a series of adventure books?

Marc. It consists of 10 books. Right now, three books are in all the major bookstores. It is about my life as an actor, but in the book I am a secret agent. The organization is called "The Order of the Cat." A little bit about the history of the book: It is for 9- to 13-year-olds. The audience gets older as I order the books and the comprehension is going to advance, so it is going to throw that audience into the older ages. This is the first series for boys since the Hardy Boys.

Q. Did you and your dad come up with the idea for the series?

Marc. Yes, we did. A few years ago, when I was in school, I would always like to read and there wasn't an adventure series for boys that really got my interest. I told my dad that we should try to come out with my own series. At first, the idea seemed kind of shaky but then my dad [thought it] made a lot of sense. We came out with the Secret Agent MJJ book series about my life as an actor/spy. I use my cover when shooting movies and they cover me to go on missions and solve all these different problems. Each book has a different story line of what I am trying to solve but everything links into the first book.

Q. Have you thought about making any of the books into movies?

Marc. Yes we are. Right now, we are in the stages of seeing how everything is going to work out—the budgeting and casting.

Q. Why do you think reading is important?

Marc. A lot of kids tell me they want to be an actor, be a rapper, or that they want to sing. You have to learn how to read in order to read the script. If you don't know how to read, you can't be an actor. Reading helps with every part of your life. When you read, it opens your mind up to other possibilities. A kid who reads for two hours a day instead of playing in a game for two hours a day has a bigger possibility of making something of his or her life.

Q. When you're filming a movie, how do you do your school work?

Marc. I have a private teacher who travels with me when we are on location. Right now, I am in 11th grade and all my schooling is online. My work and my classes are given to me through e-mail.

Q. Finally, if you could create a flavor of ice cream, what would it be and what would you call it?

Marc. I would make a flavor with chocolate, cherry bubble gum, and a little bit of vanilla. I would call it the MJ Surprise. ○

Answering the BIG Question

When you do the following activities, consider the Big Question:
Why read?

WRITE TO LEARN Think about what Marc John Jefferies says about reading. Do you agree or disagree with him? Why? Write down your ideas in your Learner's Notebook.

LITERATURE GROUPS Meet with two or three classmates who have read this selection. Discuss where Marc John Jefferies gets his ideas for writing comedy. What events in your own life might make a good story or short comedy sketch?

from

TRAVEL TEAM

by Mike Lupica

Do our genes make us what we are?

He knew he was small.

He just didn't *think* he was small.

Big difference.

Danny had known his whole life how small he was compared to everybody in his grade, from the first grade on. ❶ How he had been put in the front row, front and center, of every class picture taken. Been in the front of every line marching into every school assembly, first one through the door. Sat in the front of every classroom. Hey, little man. Hey, little guy. He was used to it by now. They'd been studying DNA in science lately; being small was in his DNA. He'd show up for soccer, or Little League baseball tryouts, or basketball, when he'd first started going to basketball tryouts at the Y, and there'd always be one of those clipboard dads who didn't know him, or his mom. Or his dad.

Asking him: "Are you sure you're with the right group, little guy?"

Meaning the right *age* group.

It happened the first time when he was eight, back when he still had to put the ball up on his shoulder and give it a heave just to get it up to a ten-foot rim. When he'd already taught himself how to lean into the bigger kid guarding him, just because there was always a bigger kid guarding him, and then step back so he could get his dopey shot off.

This was way back before he'd even tried any fancy stuff, including the crossover.

He just told the clipboard dad that he was eight, that he was little, that this was his right group, and could he have his number, please? When he told his mom about it later, she just smiled and said, "You know what you should hear when people start talking about your size? Blah blah blah."

He smiled back at her and said that he was pretty sure he would be able to remember that.

"How did you play?" she said that day, when she couldn't wait any longer for him to tell.

"I did okay."

"I have a feeling you did more than that," she said, hugging him to her. "My streak of light."

Sometimes she'd tell him how small his dad had been when he was Danny's age.

Sometimes not.

But here was the deal, when he added it all up: His height had always been much more of a stinking issue for other people, including his mom, than it was for him.

He tried not to sweat the small stuff, basically, the way grown-ups always told you.

He knew he was faster than everybody else at St. Patrick's School. And at Springs School, for that matter. Nobody on either side of town could get in front of him. He was the best passer his age, even better than Ty Ross, who was better at everything in sports than just about anybody. He knew that when it was just kids—which is the way kids always liked it in sports—and the parents were out of the gym or off the playground and you got to just play without a whistle blowing every ten seconds or somebody yelling out more instructions, he was always one of the first picked, because the other guys on his team, the shooters especially, knew he'd get them the ball. ❷

Most kids, his dad told him one time, know something about basketball that even most grown-ups never figure out.

One good passer changes everything.

Danny could pass, which is why he'd always made the team.

Almost always.

But no matter what was happening with any team he'd ever played on, no matter how tired he would be after practice, no matter how much homework he still had left, this driveway was still his special place. Like a special club with a membership of one, the place where he could come out at this time of night and imagine it up good, imagine it big and bright, even with just the one floodlight over the backboard and the other light, smaller, over the back door. His mother had done everything she could to make the driveway wider back here, even cutting into what little backyard they had the summer before last. "I told them you needed more room in the corners," she said. "The men from the paving company. They just nodded at me, like corners were some sort of <u>crucial</u> guy thing."

> **❷ Identifying Main Idea and Supporting Details**
> What makes Danny a good basketball player?

Vo·cab·u·lary
crucial (KROO shul) necessary

"Right up there with the remote control switcher for the TV," Danny said. "And leaving wet towels on the bathroom floor."

"How are the corners now?"

"Perfect," he said. "Like at the Garden."

He had just enough room in the corners now, mostly for shooting. He didn't feel as if he was trying to make a drive to the basket in his closet. Or an elevator car. He had room to _maneuver_, pretend he really *was* at the real Garden, that he was one of the small fast guys who'd made it all the way there. Like Muggsy Bogues, somebody he'd read up on when one of his coaches told him to, who was only 5' 3" and made it to the NBA. Like Tiny Archibald and Bobby Hurley and Earl Boykins, a 5' 5" guy who came out of the basketball minor leagues, another streak of light who showed everybody that more than size mattered, even in hoops. ❸

And, of course, Richie Walker.

Middletown's own.

Danny would put chairs out there and dribble through them like he was dribbling out the clock at the end of the game. Some nights he would borrow a pair of his mother's old sunglasses and tape the bottom part of the lens so he couldn't see the ball unless he looked straight down at it. This was back when he was first trying to perfect the double crossover, before he even had a chance to do it right, his hands being too little and his arms not being nearly long enough.

Sometimes he'd be so dog tired when he finished—though he would never cop to that with his mom—he'd fall into bed with his clothes on and nearly fall asleep that way.

"You done?" she'd say when she came in to say good night.

> ❸ **Understanding Graphics**
> How is the photograph on the next page related to the information in this paragraph?

Vo·cab·u·lary

maneuver (muh NOO vur) move with skill and care

"I finally got bored," he'd say, and she'd say with a smile, "I always worry about that, you getting bored by basketball."

Everybody he'd ever read up on, short or tall, had talked about how they outworked everybody else. Magic Johnson, he knew, won the championship his rookie season with the Lakers, scored forty-two points in the final game of the championship series when he had to play center because Kareem Abdul-Jabbar was hurt, then went back to East Lansing, Michigan, where he was from, in the summer and worked on his outside shooting because he'd decided it wasn't good enough.

Tonight, Danny had worked past the time when his mom usually called him in, not even noticing how cold it had gotten for October. Worked underneath the new backboard she'd gotten for him at the end of the summer. Not the only kid in his class with divorced parents now. Not the smallest kid on the court now. Just the only one. He'd drive to the basket and then hit one of the chairs with one of his lookaway passes. Or he'd step back and make a shot from the outside. Sometimes, breathing hard, like it was a real game, he'd step to the free throw line he'd drawn with chalk and make two free throws for the championship of something.

Toronto's Muggsy Bogues tries to take the ball from Washington's Mitch Richmond.

Just him and the ball and the feel of it in his hands and the whoosh of it going through the net and the sound one of the old wooden school chairs would make when he tipped it over with another bounce pass. He knew he was wearing out another pair of sneakers his mom called "old school," which to Danny always meant "on sale." Or that she had found his size at either the Nike store or the Reebok store at the factory outlet mall about forty-five minutes from Middletown, both of them knowing she couldn't afford what Athlete's Foot or Foot Locker was charging for the new Kobe sneakers from Nike, or Iverson's, or McGrady's. Or the cool new LeBron James kicks that so many of the Springs School kids were wearing this year.

He finished the way he always did, trying to cleanly execute the crossover-and-back five times in a row, low enough to the ground to be like a rock he was skipping across Taylor Lake. Five times usually making it an official good night out here.

Except.

Except this was as far from a good night as he'd ever known.

Basically, this was the worst night of his whole life.

❧

Danny's mother, Ali, watched him from his bedroom window on the second floor, standing to the side of the window in the dark room, trying not to let him see her up here, even though she could see him sneaking a look occasionally, especially when he'd do something fine down on the court, sink a long one or make a left-handed layup or execute that tricky dribble he was always working on.

Sometimes he'd do it right and come right out of it and be on his way to the basket, so fast she thought he should leave a puff of smoke like one of those old Road Runner cartoons.

Gosh, you're getting old, she thought. Did kids even know who the Road Runner was anymore?

"Nice work with that double dribble," she'd tell him sometimes when he finally came in the house, tired even if he'd never admit that to her.

"Mom, you *know* it's not a double dribble. *This*"—showing her on the kitchen floor with the ball that was on its way up to his room with him—"is a double *crossover*."

"Whatever it is," she'd say, "don't do it in the kitchen."

That would get a smile out of her boy sometimes.

The boy who had cried when he told her his news tonight. ❹

He was twelve now. And never let her see him cry unless he took a bad spill in a game or in the driveway, or got himself all tied up because he was afraid he was going to fail some test, even though he never did.

❹ Setting a Purpose for Reading
What do you want to find out about Danny now?

But tonight her son cried in the living room and let her hug him as she told him she hoped this was the worst thing that ever happened to him.

"If it is," she said, "you're going to have an even happier life than I imagined for you."

She pushed back a little and smoothed out some of his blond hair, spikey now because he'd been wearing one of his four thousand baseball caps while he played.

"What do I always tell you?" she said.

Without looking up at her, reciting it like she was helping him learn his part in a school play, Danny said, "Nobody imagines up things better than you do."

"There you go."

Another one of their games.

Except on this night he suddenly said, "So how come you can't imagine a happier life for us *now*?"

Then he got up from the couch and ran out of the room and the next thing she heard was the bounce of the ball in the driveway. Like the real beat of his heart.

Or their lives.

She waited a while, cleaned up their dinner dishes, even though that never took long with just the two of them, finished correcting some test papers. Then she went up to his room and watched him try to play through this, the twelve-year-old who went through life being asked if he was ten, or nine, or eight.

Ali saw what she always saw, even tonight, when he was out here with the fierce expression on his face, hardly ever smiling, even as he dreamed his dreams, imagining for himself now, imagining up a happy life for himself, one where he wasn't always the smallest. One where all people saw was the size of his talent, all that speed, all the magic things he could do with a basketball in either hand.

No matter how much she tried not to, she saw all his father in him.

❧

He was all the way past the house, on his way to making the right on Cleveland Avenue, when he saw the light at the end of the driveway, and saw the little boy back there.

He stopped the car.

Or maybe it stopped itself.

He was good at blaming, why not blame the car?

What was that old movie where Jack Nicholson played the retired astronaut? He couldn't remember the name, just that Shirley MacLaine was in it, too, and she was going around with Jack, and then her daughter got sick and the whole thing turned into a major chick flick.

There was this scene where Nicholson was trying to leave town, but the daughter was sick, and even though he didn't care about too much other than having fun, he couldn't leave because Shirley MacLaine needed him.

You think old Jack is out of there, adios, and then he shows up at the door, that smile on his face, and says, "Almost a clean getaway."

He used to think his life was a movie. Enough people used to tell him that it was.

He parked near the corner of Cleveland and Earl, then walked halfway back up the block, across the street from 422 Earl, still wondering what he was doing on this street tonight, cruising this neighborhood, in this stupid small small-minded town.

Watching this kid play ball.

<u>Mesmerized</u>, watching the way this kid, about as tall as his bad hip, could handle a basketball.

Watching him shoot his funny shot, pushing the ball off his shoulder like he was pushing a buddy over a fence. He seemed to miss as many shots as he made. But he *never* missed the folding chairs he was obviously using as imaginary teammates, whether he was looking at them when he fired one of his passes. Or not.

Watching the kid stop after a while, rearrange the chairs now, turning them into defenders, dribbling through them, controlling the ball better with his right hand than his left, keeping the ball low, only struggling when he tried to get tricky and double up on a crossover move.

The kid stopping sometimes, breathing hard, going through his little routine before making a couple of free throws. Like it was all some complicated game being played inside the kid's head.

He hadn't heard anybody coming, so he nearly jumped out of his skin when she tapped him on the shoulder, jumping back a little until he saw who it was.

"Why don't you go over?" Ali said.

"You shouldn't sneak up on people that way."

Vo·cab·u·lary

mesmerized (MEZ mur yzd) fascinated

"No," she said, "*you* shouldn't sneak up on people that way."

"I was going to call tomorrow," he said.

"Boy," she said, "I don't think I've ever heard that one before."

Ali said, "You can catch me up later on the fascinating comings and goings of your life. Right now, this is one of those nights in his life when he needs his father, Rich. To go with about a thousand others."

Richie Walker noticed she wasn't looking at him, she was facing across the street the way he was, watching Danny.

"Why tonight in particular?"

"He didn't make travel team," she said now on the quiet, dark street. "*Your* travel team."

"Look at him play. How could he not make travel?"

"They told him he was too small." **5** ○

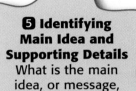

5 Identifying Main Idea and Supporting Details
What is the main idea, or message, of this story?

Answering the BIG Question

When you do the following activities, consider the Big Question:
Why read?

WRITE TO LEARN Think about how Danny deals with the challenges he faces. Have you or has someone you know ever tried to overcome an obstacle through hard work? Write about the experience in your Learner's Notebook.

PARTNER TALK Pair with a partner who has read the excerpt from *Travel Team.* Discuss how reading this selection affected you. Which character or characters did you admire most? Least? Why?

Silent Dance
DANCING WITH THE DEAF

by Nancy Bo Flood

Don't be surprised when a deaf or wheelchair-bound student wins the next dance contest.

You don't have to hear in order to dance. ❶ Many kids who are deaf love to move, twist, and turn with the music—they feel the beat. Like anyone else, they can become dancers—modern, ballet, or dancing just for the fun of it.

Zenon Dance Company in Minneapolis, Minnesota, teaches dance to deaf students.

> **❶ Setting a Purpose for Reading**
> What do you expect to learn from reading this article?

Megan Flood, a <u>professional</u> dancer and teacher, explains, "What a surprise to discover that students who are deaf often learn dancing faster than students who hear."

"Movement is part of the daily language for the deaf," Flood says. "Their talking is physical and visual. They talk with their hands and then watch . . . when the other person answers. When a hearing person starts learning to dance, it is often new and uncomfortable to show what you feel by moving your body. The deaf do this all the time. Also, the deaf watch intensely. Their eyes are their . . . windows to the world. . . . These skills are important 'learning to dance' skills."

So, feel that beat and . . . dance!

Dancers on Wheels

by Janeen R. Adil

Annie had her first dance lesson when she was nine years old and in third grade. The students watched her come in, and even the grownups looked at her. She heard people whisper, "That girl can't dance. She can't even walk."

Annie knew they were wrong, and so did her teacher.

Vo•cab•u•lary

professional (pruh FESH uh nul) earning a living in a job

They knew that dancing, just like painting or playing music, comes from the heart. Annie didn't need to move her feet—she could dance by moving her strong arms and body. Her wheelchair would become part of the dance.

Every week, Annie went to her dance lesson with Miss Karen. First Annie warmed up her muscles by stretching up and down and side to side. Then her teacher put on some music. When the music was fast, Annie loved to twirl, spinning her wheelchair in circles. When the music was slow, Annie moved her arms like a graceful swan. Annie practiced for months to get ready for a dance show. She picked out her own music and costume. When the big night finally came, Annie was nervous but excited, too. When it was her turn, she gave Miss Karen a happy smile and thought proudly, "I am a dancer!" Then Annie wheeled out onto the stage and began to dance.

Kitty Lunn is someone who understands Annie's experience. She was 8 when she decided to be a dancer. By the time she was 15, Kitty was dancing with the New Orleans Civic Ballet. She studied with famous teachers and danced in widely known ballets such as *Swan Lake* and *The Nutcracker*. When she was older, Kitty moved to New York City, where she worked as an actress and a dancer. She was getting ready to perform in her first Broadway show when her life changed forever.

While hurrying to rehearsal, Kitty slipped on some ice. She fell down a flight of stairs and broke her back. The accident left her a paraplegic (pa-ruh-PLEE-jik). This means she can move her arms and body but not her legs. It also means that Kitty now uses a wheelchair to get around.

At first, Kitty thought her life as a dancer was over. Then she learned something important. "The dancer inside me," she says, "didn't know or care that I was using a wheelchair. She just wanted to keep dancing." So Kitty found a way to continue doing what she loved.

In 1994, Kitty Lunn started Infinity Dance Theater. Its members are dancers with and without disabilities. They use movements from ballet, modern dance, and jazz. Like some of the other dancers, Kitty uses a special lightweight wheelchair.

When the 1996 Olympics were held in Atlanta, Georgia, Kitty was there. She performed a dance called "Inside My Body There Is a Dancer." This title is a good description of what Kitty believes. The Infinity dancers perform all over the world. They also help dance teachers learn to work with students who have disabilities.

There are many other dance companies that include both wheelchair and standing dancers. Each of them would agree with Kitty's advice when she says, "Listen to the dancer in your heart." There's always a way to dance! ❷ ○

❷ **Understanding Graphics**
How do the photographs on pages 16 and 17 help you understand "Dancers on Wheels"?

Answering the BIG Question

As you do the following activities, consider the Big Question:
Why read?

WRITE TO LEARN Annie and Kitty both found a way to dance—even though some people thought they couldn't. In your Learner's Notebook, write about a time when you did something that others doubted you could do.

LITERATURE GROUPS Meet with two or three classmates who have read both articles. Discuss other people you know about who have done what they wanted to do, despite illness or disability. How have these people inspired you?

Mario and His Fields of Dreams

from *The Macmillan Book of Baseball Stories*
by Terry Egan, Stan Friedmann, and Mike Levine

Did Mario really strike out when he quit professional baseball?

Mario's parents sailed from Salerno, Italy, in search of the great America. They found it in 1925. As their boat passed the Statue of Liberty, they saw in the distance the busy avenues of New York City.

Maybe the streets weren't paved with gold, but the parents believed this was the land of opportunity. Through study and hard work, a poor man's child could become a doctor, a judge, even a governor.

Mario's father dug ditches. He sold fruit from a <u>pushcart</u>. He saved pennies and opened a small grocery store in the south Jamaica neighborhood of Queens.

Mario was the second of three children. He saw how hard his parents worked, sunup to sundown. Every day they told him, "Study. Study hard. You can be somebody. There is a place for you in the great American dream."

Mario was a good student. He enjoyed learning. What he really loved, though, was the great American game: baseball. It was all around him, in the streets of New York, in the crackling sounds of Dodger <u>broadcasts</u> on the family radio, in the Polo Grounds, at Ebbets Field, and Yankee Stadium, the homes of New York's teams.

After school he'd roam the playgrounds of Queens, playing center field. Whether he was sliding into second base to break up a double play or <u>sprinting</u> back for fly balls, Mario played hard, real hard.

He was a teenager when he played for a traveling team from his neighborhood. They went to Fort Monmouth, New Jersey, to play a game against a special services team of army ballplayers. The pitcher was Whitey Ford, the rookie <u>sensation</u> from the New York Yankees.

Watching on the <u>sidelines</u> was Pittsburgh Pirates scout Ed McCarric. He couldn't take his eyes off the young center fielder. The kid could hit and throw and run. After the game McCarric

---

Vo·cab·u·lary

pushcart (PUSH kart) a light cart pushed by hand, sometimes used to sell things
broadcasts (BRAWD castz) radio or television programs
sprinting (SPRINT ing) running at top speed for a short distance
sensation (sen SAY shun) an outstanding person causing excitement
sidelines (SYD lynz) along the sides of an athletic field

told Mario he wanted to sign him up. **❶**

McCarric said he'd give Mario a
$2,000 signing bonus. Mario couldn't
believe it. That was a ton of money.
Mickey Mantle only got $1,100 to sign
with the Yankees a few years before.

❶ Scanning
Scan this page for
key words that show
the obstacles Mario
faced in accepting
McCarric's offer.

He couldn't wait to get home to tell
his father. Because he was underage—
still in high school—he needed his father to
sign the contract. He was certain his dad would.

His folks worked hard. They could use the money. And Mario
would get to play baseball. He saw this as a road to his great
American dream.

His father shook his head. "Don't they play baseball in the
summer, before school ends?" he asked.

"Well, yeah, Pops, but—"

"No," said his father. "Absolutely not."

Mario couldn't believe it. McCarric couldn't believe it. He
begged Branch Rickey, the Pirates president, not to let this kid get
away. He could be the best <u>prospect</u> in the whole organization.

If there was one thing Branch Rickey valued in this world, it
was baseball talent. Just five years earlier he had signed up Jackie
Robinson, who became the major leagues' first African-American
ball player.

All Rickey cared about was whether a kid could play ball.
Mario could, and Rickey wanted him. He wrote a personal letter
to Mario's father: "I admire you for wanting your child to get an
education. And as head of this outfit, I can promise you that your
son will not have to play ball for us until after his classes end."

His father still wasn't convinced. He was worried his son
would forget about college and only care about baseball.

Vo•cab•u•lary

prospect (PRAWS pekt) a person likely to be chosen for something

Mario was desperate. He wanted to play ball so badly, but he knew he had to listen to his father.

McCarric paid a personal visit to the family grocery store. Under the hanging sticks of <u>provolone</u> and salami, McCarric pleaded with Mario's father: "Don't worry. We'll make sure he doesn't touch a baseball until his classes are over."

The father looked at Mario. "Do you promise you'll stay with your education and that you'll go to college?"

"Yes, Pops. I give you my word."

His father signed the contract.

In 1952, after graduating from high school, Mario reported to the minor league Brunswick Pirates in Georgia. He played center field. He hit okay: .252. He showed a lot of power. He played hard. He noticed how good the rest of the players were and how hard he would have to work to make it to the major leagues. But he loved it.

Then, during a game late in the season, Mario ran into trouble. He had gotten two hits off a pitcher named Ed Barbier. The next time up, Barbier meant to brush Mario back from the plate. But the pitch was too far inside. The ball hit Mario in the head.

Vo·cab·u·lary

provolone (proh voh LOHN) a type of firm, smoked cheese from Italy

In the hospital for a month, he had plenty of time to think. He remembered going to Yankee Stadium a few years back to see Joe DiMaggio play. Now, that was a ball player. That was greatness. Sure, Mario loved baseball. But he figured he was never going to be Joe DiMaggio.

Because Mario had studied hard in school, St. John's University in Queens was offering him an academic scholarship. He was all alone with a big decision to make. He thought of baseball and he thought of the promise he had made to his father. Mario decided to drop baseball and his dream of a major league career so that he could go to college. ❷

Mario continued to love the game, but he never did go on to play center field for the Pittsburgh Pirates. He probably would have been too busy anyway. On November 5, 1982, Mario M. Cuomo was elected the fifty-second governor of the state of New York.

❷ **Identifying Main Idea and Supporting Details** Why did Mario decide to quit baseball and go to college?

His father was right about this great country. There is more than one <u>avenue</u> to the American dream. ○

Answering the BIG Question

As you do the following activities, consider the Big Question:
Why read?

WRITE TO LEARN Think of a time when you had to choose between two things you really wanted to do. Why did you choose one over the other? Write down your thoughts in your Learner's Notebook.

PARTNER TALK Meet with another student who has read this selection. Have you ever imagined yourselves as professional athletes? What sacrifices would you make to pursue your dream?

Vo•cab•u•lary

avenue (AV uh nyoo) a means of getting something

KIDS VOTING USA

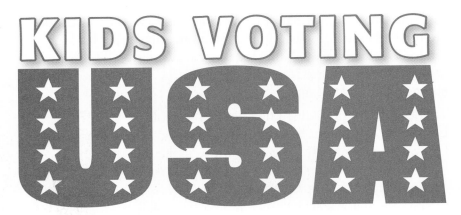

by Katherine House

Psst, spread the word—did you know that you have the power to affect a presidential election?

More than 15 years ago, three friends went fishing together in Costa Rica, a country in Central America. When they came back from their trip, they had more than fish. They also brought information they hoped would change elections in the United States. ❶

Bob Evans was one of the three friends. He remembers the trip well. Costa Rica had just held a big election. Evans was surprised to learn that almost 90 percent of eligible voters (nine out of every ten) had voted. He knew that many Americans do not vote. In fact, in the 2000 presidential election, only five out of every ten voters voted. In other words, only half of the Americans who could vote, did vote.

❶ **Setting a Purpose for Reading**
What kind of information do you hope to learn from this selection?

Why do so many Costa Ricans vote? Evans discovered that kids have something to do with it. In Costa Rica, it's a <u>tradition</u> for parents to take their children with them when they vote. This simple act does two things: It encourages adults to vote, and it teaches children that voting is important. Schools play a <u>role</u>, too. Beginning in kindergarten, Costa Rican children learn about elections every year.

The three fishing friends came up with a big idea. They wanted to do the same thing in the United States that Costa Ricans do. They wanted children to go to the <u>polls</u>. So they started a program called Kids Voting USA.

Vo•cab•u•lary

tradition (truh DIH shun) a belief or custom that is handed down within a culture
role (rohl) a function or part performed in a particular process
polls (polz) places where votes are cast or recorded

Kids Voting USA is for kids from kindergarten through high school. In 2003, more than 4 million students took part in Kids Voting USA. In class, students learn about elections and voting. They talk about important <u>issues</u>. And when students talk about elections at home, parents learn, too. "Parents have to do homework and do some thinking on their own," says Bob Evans.

Then, on Election Day, Kids Voting USA students vote. Kids go with an adult to the polls, where special <u>ballots</u> let them choose their candidates. Although kids' votes are not counted with adult votes, newspapers usually report the results of the Kids Voting elections.

The result is a winning program for everyone. Experts say that more adults vote in places where Kids Voting USA holds elections. Just as in Costa Rica, children in the United States are helping to get voters to the polls. ❷ ○

> **❷ Identifying Main Idea**
> What is the most important idea in this article?

Answering the
BIG Question

As you do the following activities, consider the Big Question:
Why read?

WRITE TO LEARN Were you surprised that a small Central American country has a higher voter turnout than the United States? Write a brief entry in your Learner's Notebook about possible reasons that so many Americans choose not to vote.

LITERATURE GROUPS Meet with two or three others who have read "Kids Voting USA." Discuss how people decide whom to vote for. Do you think that getting information from newspapers and magazines is better than getting information from TV?

Vo·cab·u·lary

issues (ISH yoos) matters of public concern
ballots (BAL utz) sheets of paper used to cast a secret vote

33

35

THE DARE

by Nikki Grimes

What makes a person tough?

Dear Zuri,

The kids here pretend to be tougher than they are.
I ignore it mostly, 'cause they're nice in their own way.
Besides, I think they may just be trying to impress the "city kid."

Today they dared me to climb up into a tree, and, of course, I did.
Then they yelled, "Okay, Miss Big-Town Brown, jump down."
Now, my mother taught me to use my head for more than a hat rack.

So, I climbed back down and said, "A dare is fine with me,
but jumping from a tree is stupid, and I'm no fool."
Then I heard someone whisper, "She's pretty cool—
for a city girl." ○

Answering the BIG Question

As you do the following activities, consider the Big Question:
Why read?

WRITE TO LEARN Think about the speaker's decision not to jump down from the tree. Write a brief entry in your Learner's Notebook reflecting on what really makes a person tough.

LITERATURE GROUPS Meet with two or three classmates who have read "The Dare." Discuss why people dare others and why people sometimes do foolish things on a dare.

Who Turned on the Faucet?

by Sarah E. Romanov

Do cry for me, and please tell me why! ❶

Y ou walk into the kitchen while someone is chopping onions. A cold wind hits you in the face when you turn a corner on the street. You fall off your bike and scrape your knee. You watch a sad movie with your friends. What do all of these things have in common? They can all turn on the faucets in your eyes, sending rivers of warm tears flowing down your cheeks! Your tears might embarrass you at times, but they're very important to your eyes.

> **❶ Skimming**
> Read the first paragraph and then look over the rest of the selection to get a general overview.

Tear glands under your upper eyelids are responsible for making tears, which are made of water, <u>proteins</u>, <u>hormones</u>, and a special oil that helps protect your eyes. If you've ever tasted

---

Vo•cab•u•lary

proteins (PROH teenz) basic elements that can be found in foods such as meat, fish, eggs, and beans
hormones (HOR monz) substances made of body tissue that help the body function in a healthy and normal way

your tears, you know they're also salty.

As tears wash down over your eyeballs, they drain out through tear ducts—tiny tubes that run between your eyes and nose. Look in a mirror and pull down your lower eyelid a bit. Do you see a little hole in the corner near your nose? That's the opening of a tear duct. If your eyes are watering, those tear ducts keep the flow under control. But if you start to cry, the ducts can't drain the tears quickly enough so they overflow, running down your face. Because tear ducts connect your eyes and nose, when your eyes water and your nose gets runny, you grab a tissue and blow out . . . tears! That's right, those are tears that have drained from your eyes into your nose.

Shedding tears is your body's way of giving your eyes the protection and moisture they need. In fact, you constantly make just enough tears to make sure your eyes aren't too dry. Blinking coats the eyes with this special <u>moisturizer</u>, called continuous tears, all day long.

Other tears called reflex tears flow to protect your eyes from things that aren't supposed to be in them. That is why you get teary-eyed when it's windy. Your eyes know that wind can dry them out fast, so they do their best to keep things wet! And when a piece of sand or an eyelash gets into your eye, those faucets turn on full-force to wash the invader out. So why does just the smell of onions make your eyes water? It's not really the smell— when an onion is cut, it releases chemicals that irritate your eyes. **2**

2 Identifying Main Idea
What is the main point the article makes about reflex tears?

Emotional tears are the least understood kind of tears. They flow when you watch a sad movie, get angry with someone, are very afraid, or even receive exciting news that makes you happy. Sometimes just seeing someone crying can make you cry, even if you don't feel sad yourself. Some

Vo•cab•u•lary

moisturizer (MOYS chuh ry zur) a liquid that helps relieve dryness

people cry easily, while others have a hard time shedding tears.

Among others, Dr. William Frey, a scientist from Minnesota, has spent many years studying tears. When Dr. Frey needed samples of tears to study, volunteers watched sad movies and collected their tears in little bottles for him. He discovered that emotional tears contain larger amounts of certain chemicals and hormones than the other types of tears do. Your body produces these <u>substances</u> in response to stress.

When people are very stressed and have too many of these hormones and chemicals in their bodies, they can become sick, both physically and emotionally. Dr. Frey believes that <u>shedding</u> emotional tears releases these bad substances and helps maintain your body's proper chemical balance. This might explain why you feel better after a good cry.

There are still many mysteries about tears and crying that future research might explain. Scientists like Dr. Frey are working very hard to solve these mysteries. In the meantime, whenever you blink your eyes, smell freshly cut onions, or watch a sad movie, grab a tissue and be thankful for the wonderful way tears help take care of your body! ○

Answering the BIG Question

As you do the following activities, consider the Big Question:
Why read?

WRITE TO LEARN Think about a time when you shed emotional tears. Write a brief entry in your Learner's Notebook describing what made you cry and how you felt afterward.

PARTNER TALK Meet with another student who has read this selection. Think about other ways the body protects itself. Make a list of all the ways that come to mind.

Vo•cab•u•lary

substances (SUB stuns uz) kinds of material from which something is made
shedding (SHED ing) pouring out

The Red Lion

by Diane Wolkstein

Boy, some princes have all the luck—sure, they have to fight a lion before becoming king . . . WHAT?!

When the king of <u>Persia</u> died, there was great weeping, for he had been a brave and wise leader. Yet in little more than a month the <u>mourning</u> would be over, and the king's son would be crowned. But before the prince could be crowned, he would have to prove his courage, just as every prince before him had done, by fighting the Red Lion. **❶**

> **❶ Setting a Purpose for Reading**
> What do you want to find out as you read this story?

Vo•cab•u•lary

Persia (PUR zhuh) former name for Iran
mourning (MORN ing) showing signs of grief for a death

The Red Lion

One day during this time the <u>vizier</u> went to the young prince and <u>urged</u> him to prepare himself for the contest. The prince trembled. He had always been afraid of lions, and the Red Lion was the most ferocious of lions. So the prince decided to run away.

That night when it was very dark, he crept out of his bedroom, mounted his horse, and rode off. He rode two days and nights. On the morning of the third day he entered a <u>grove</u> of trees and heard a sweet melody. Dismounting, he walked quietly until he saw a shepherd, sitting in a clearing and playing a flute. All about the shepherd the sheep stood listening.

"God be with you," said the shepherd to the stranger.

"And with you," the prince replied, "but please do not stop your song."

The shepherd took up his flute and played for the clouds, for the winds, for his sheep, and for the stranger.

When he finished, the prince spoke: "Surely you are wondering who I am. I wish I could tell you my name. But it is a secret that must stay locked in my heart. I beg you to believe me; I am no enemy. I am an honorable youth who has been forced to flee from his home."

"You are welcome to stay with me," the shepherd answered. "I would be glad of your company, and I can show you a place that will cause you to forget your troubles."

Hour after hour the prince and the shepherd walked, the prince leading his horse and the sheep following behind the shepherd. As the sun was setting, they came to the most beautiful valley the prince had ever seen. It was perfectly quiet, and the prince and the shepherd sat and gazed in wonder at the hills in front of them. Suddenly the shepherd jumped up.

"Time to go!" he said.

"But why must we leave so quickly?" asked the prince. "Can

Vo•cab•u•lary

vizier (vih ZEER) a high officer of various Muslim countries
urged (urjd) moved to action, effort, or speed
grove (grohv) a small wood without underbrush

there be any place on earth more lovely?"

"It is beautiful," the shepherd agreed. And then he raised his sleeve, revealing a long, cruel red scar. He traced his finger along the scar and said, "Lions! Once I was late returning to the village, and the village gates were closed. This is the result. I do not want it to happen a second time."

"Please return to the village with the sheep," the prince said. "I cannot go with you." He mounted his horse and rode north. He rode two days and nights, and on the third morning he came to a desert. ❷

❷ **Scanning**
Scan the selection to see how many times the prince tries to avoid lions.

He and his horse were tired and hungry and thirsty, and the wind blew sand in the prince's face. Suddenly his horse neighed. Through the streaming sands he saw the tents of an Arab camp. His horse began to prance, but the prince pulled back on the bridle and continued to ride slowly to show that his was a peaceful visit.

An Arab <u>sheik</u> greeted him with <u>courtesy</u>. He offered the prince food and made sure his horse was fed and cared for. After the prince had eaten, he said to the sheik, "Forgive me if I do not reveal my name. Because of certain troubles it is a secret that must stay locked in my heart. But I have jewels and precious stones I would gladly give you if you would allow me to remain with you."

"You are our guest," the sheik replied, and he refused to accept any of the prince's treasures.

The following morning the sheik provided the prince with a magnificent stallion, and for the next three days the prince rode with the sheik and his companions, hunting antelope.

On the third evening the sheik spoke to the prince. "My men are pleased with your spirit," he said, "and with your skill at hunting. But there will soon be a battle. My men want to know if they can rely on

Vo•cab•u•lary
sheik (sheek) an Arab chief
courtesy (KUR tuh see) polite behavior

your strength and courage. To the south lies a range of hills known as the Red Hills. It is lion country. Ride there tomorrow on the stallion. Take your sword and spear, and bring us back the hide of a lion to show us we can count on you on the day of battle."

That night when it was very still, the prince slipped out of his tent. He stroked the beloved stallion he had ridden and whispered goodbye in his ear. Then he mounted his own horse and rode west.

After two days and nights he came to a country of rolling meadows and green fields. There in the distance he saw a splendid red sandstone palace. At the gates the prince took off his ring and asked the guard to present it to the <u>emir</u>. Immediately the prince was invited to enter the palace.

As he was explaining his situation to the emir, Perizide, the emir's daughter, appeared. The emir, who was impressed with the prince's good manners and fine speech, said to his daughter, "My child, please show this young man our palace and gardens, and invite him to the entertainment this evening."

Perizide led the prince through room after room and then out to the garden, where flowers and trees of every kind grew. In the middle of the garden was an oval pool filled with rose water, and in the water floated a lily. It was perfect—and yet not as beautiful as Perizide.

After dinner in the cool evening air, Perizide provided the entertainment, playing the <u>lute</u> and singing. As the prince listened, he felt his soul rising higher and higher. *That is why I have run away,* he thought, *so I might find Perizide.*

"Rrraaagggh!"

"What was that?" cried the prince, jumping to his feet.

"Oh, that's just our guard Boulak. He's yawning."

"Yawning?" repeated the prince.

"Yes," said Perizide. "He does that when it is late. I will say goodnight now."

Vo•cab•u•lary

emir (ih MEER) a ruler or chief in Islamic countries
lute (loot) a type of stringed instrument with a large, pear-shaped body

After she left, the emir stood up. "It is late for me, too. Come. I will show you to your bedroom."

They had just begun to climb the staircase when the prince looked up. His hand froze on the banister. There at the top of the landing stood an enormous lion.

"Oh, that's just Boulak," said the emir. "He's perfectly harmless. He never attacks unless someone is afraid of him."

"Oh, I'm not, ah, quite r-r-ready for, ah, s-s-sleep," stammered the prince.

"Well, then, come up when you wish," said the emir. "Yours is the first room on the right."

The prince backed down the stairs. He backed down the corridor, into the music room, and locked the doors. He sat on a chair and waited. Soon he heard the lion padding down the stairs. He heard him claw at the door. The door shook. The lion roared "Rrraaagggh!"

The prince thought the lion would tear down the door and devour him, but he just sat there. He did not try to run away. The lion roared again. "Rrraaagggh!"

The prince listened. The lion roared a third time. Suddenly the prince realized that the roars were not threats—they were warnings. They were telling him, "Three times you have run away. If you run away again—wherever you may go—a lion will be waiting." A lion would always be waiting for the prince until he went home to fight his own lion.

The prince listened. Boulak did not roar again. Then the prince heard the lion padding back up the stairs.

Early the next morning the prince explained that he had to return home

47

at once. He mounted his horse and, thinking only of the Red Lion, rode day and night until he reached the palace.

At the appointed time the prince entered the crowded arena. The emir, Perizide, the sheik, and the shepherd were all there, seated in the stands. But the prince did not look up. No, his eyes were on the doors from which the Red Lion would <u>emerge</u>. He waited.

The doors opened. The lion sprang out. The prince stood firm, his spear in his hand. The lion roared and leapt—right over the prince's head. When the prince whirled around to throw his spear, he saw the Red Lion lying on his back, waving his paws in the air like a playful puppy. Then the lion trotted up to him and affectionately licked his hands.

The Red Lion was tame. Every lion that had ever fought a prince of Persia had been tame—only fear would make him ferocious.

So the prince was crowned king of Persia. In due time he married Perizide, and the two lived together happily and ruled their kingdom wisely and well. ○

Answering the BIG Question

As you do the following activities, consider the Big Question:
Why read?

WRITE TO LEARN Have you ever faced some fears over and over again, just like the prince? Write a brief entry in your Learner's Notebook about how you handled those fears. Afterward, did anything in your life change?

LITERATURE GROUPS Meet with two or three others who have read "The Red Lion." Discuss and list all the reasons why you would or would not want to be a prince or princess. Which list is longer?

Vo•cab•u•lary

emerge (ih MURJ) come out into view

THE MAKING OF A
SCIENTIST

from *What Do You Care What Other People Think?*
by Richard P. Feynman as told to Ralph Leighton

How did a Nobel Prize-winning scientist get his start by talking to his dad about tiles, birds, and wagons?

Before I was born, my father told my mother, "If it's a boy, he's going to be a scientist."[1] When I was just a little kid, very small in a highchair, my father brought home a lot of little bathroom tiles—seconds—of different colors. We played with them, my father setting them up vertically on my highchair like

....

[1] Richard's younger sister, Joan, has a Ph.D. in physics, in spite of this preconception that only boys are destined to be scientists.

dominoes, and I would push one end so they would all go down. ❶

Then after a while, I'd help set them up. Pretty soon, we're setting them up in a more complicated way: two white tiles and a blue tile, two white tiles and a blue tile, and so on. When my mother saw that she said, "Leave the poor child alone. If he wants to put a blue tile, let him put a blue tile."

But my father said, "No, I want to show him what patterns are like and how interesting they are. It's a kind of elementary mathematics." So he started very early to tell me about the world and how interesting it is.

❶ **Skimming**
Skim this selection to get a general idea of what it's about.

We had the *Encyclopaedia Britannica* at home. When I was a small boy he used to sit me on his lap and read to me from the *Britannica*. We would be reading, say, about dinosaurs. It would be talking about the *Tyrannosaurus rex*, and it would say something like, "This dinosaur is twenty-five feet high and its head is six feet across."

My father would stop reading and say, "Now, let's see what that means. That would mean that if he stood in our front yard, he would be tall enough to put his head through our window up here." (We were on the second floor.) "But his head would be too wide to fit in the window." Everything he read to me he would translate as best he could into some reality.

It was very exciting and very, very interesting to think there were animals of such <u>magnitude</u>—and that they all died out, and that nobody knew why. I wasn't frightened that there would be one coming in my window as a <u>consequence</u> of this. But I learned from my father to translate: everything I read I try to figure out what it really means, what it's really saying.

We used to go to the Catskill Mountains, a place where people from New York City would go in the summer. The fathers would all return to New York to work during the week, and come back only for the weekend. On weekends, my father would take me for walks in the woods, and he'd tell me about interesting things that were going on in the woods. When the other mothers saw this, they thought it was wonderful and that the other fathers should take their sons for walks. They tried to work on them, but they didn't get anywhere at first. They wanted my father to take all the kids, but he didn't want to because he had a special relationship with me. So it ended up that the other fathers had to take their children for walks the next weekend.

The next Monday, when the fathers were all back at work, we kids were playing in a field. One kid says to me, "See that bird? What kind of bird is that?"

I said, "I haven't the slightest idea what kind of a bird it is."

He says, "It's a brown-throated thrush. Your father doesn't teach you anything!"

But it was the opposite. He had already taught me: "See that bird?" he says. "It's a Spencer's warbler." (I knew he didn't know the real name.) "Well, in Italian, it's a *Chutto Lapittida*. In Portuguese, it's a *Bom da Peida*. In Chinese, it's a *Chung-long-tah*, and in Japanese, it's a *Katano Tekeda*. You can know the name of that bird in all the languages of the world, but when you're finished, you'll know absolutely nothing whatever about the bird. You'll only know about humans in different places, and what they call the bird.

Vo•cab•u•lary

magnitude (MAG nih tood) great size or extent
consequence (KAWN sih kwens) a logical conclusion

So let's look at the bird and see what it's *doing*—that's what counts." (I learned very early the difference between knowing the name of something and knowing something.)

He says, "For example, look: the bird pecks at its feathers all the time. See it walking around, pecking at its feathers?"

"Yeah."

He says, "Why do you think birds peck at their feathers?"

I said, "Well, maybe they mess up their feathers when they fly, so they're pecking them in order to straighten them out."

"All right," he says. "If that were the case, then they would peck a lot just after they've been flying. Then, after they've been on the ground a while, they wouldn't peck so much any more— you know what I mean?"

"Yeah."

He says, "Let's look and see if they peck more just after they land."

It wasn't hard to tell: there was not much difference between the birds that had been walking around a bit and those that had just landed. So I said, "I give up. Why does a bird peck at its feathers?"

"Because there are lice bothering it," he says. "The lice eat flakes of protein that come off its feathers."

He continued, "Each louse has some waxy stuff on its legs, and little mites eat that. The mites don't digest it perfectly, so they <u>emit</u> from their rear ends a sugar-like material, in which bacteria grow."

Vo•cab•u•lary

emit (ee MIT) to throw or give off or out

Finally he says, "So you see, everywhere there's a source of food, there's *some* form of life that finds it."

Now, I knew that it may not have been exactly a louse, that it might not be exactly true that the louse's legs have mites. The story was probably incorrect in *detail*, but what he was telling me was right <u>in principle</u>.

Another time, when I was older, he picked a leaf off of a tree. This leaf had a flaw, a thing we never look at much. The leaf was sort of deteriorated; it had a little brown line in the shape of a C, starting somewhere in the middle of the leaf and going out in a curl to the edge.

"Look at this brown line," he says. "It's narrow at the beginning and it's wider as it goes to the edge. What this is, is a fly—a blue fly with yellow eyes and green wings has come and laid an egg on this leaf. Then, when the egg hatches into a maggot (a caterpillar-like thing), it spends its whole life eating this leaf—that's where it gets its food. As it eats along, it leaves behind this brown trail of eaten leaf. As the maggot grows, the trail grows wider until he's grown to full size at the end of the leaf, where he turns into a fly—a blue fly with yellow eyes and green wings—who flies away and lays an egg on another leaf."

Again, I knew that the details weren't precisely correct—it could have even been a beetle—but the idea that he was trying to explain to me was the amusing part of life: the whole thing is just reproduction. No matter how complicated the business is, the main point is to do it again! ❷

Not having experience with many fathers, I didn't realize how <u>remarkable</u> he was. How did he learn the deep principles of science and the love of it, what's behind it, and why it's worth

❷ **Identifying Main Idea**
What does Richard's father teach him by using the example of the leaf?

Vo·cab·u·lary

in principle (in PRIN suh pul) in regard to the basics
remarkable (rih MARK uh bul) uncommon or extraordinary

doing? I never really asked him, because I just assumed that those were things that fathers knew.

My father taught me to notice things. One day, I was playing with an "express wagon," a little wagon with a railing around it. It had a ball in it, and when I pulled the wagon, I noticed something about the way the ball moved.

I went to my father and said, "Say, Pop, I noticed something. When I pull the wagon, the ball rolls to the back of the wagon. And when I'm pulling it along and I suddenly stop, the ball rolls to the front of the wagon. Why is that?"

"That, nobody knows," he said. "The general principle is that things which are moving tend to keep on moving, and things which are standing still tend to stand still, unless you push them hard. This tendency is called 'inertia,' but nobody knows why it's true." Now, that's a deep understanding. He didn't just give me the name.

He went on to say, "If you look from the side, you'll see that it's the back of the wagon that you're pulling against the ball, and the ball stands still. As a matter of fact, from the <u>friction</u> it starts to move

Richard P. Feynman

Vo•cab•u•lary

friction (FRIK shun) the rubbing of one object or surface against another

forward a little bit in relation to the ground. It doesn't move back."

I ran back to the little wagon and set the ball up again and pulled the wagon. Looking sideways, I saw that indeed he was right. Relative to the sidewalk, it moved forward a little bit.

That's the way I was educated by my father, with those kinds of examples and discussions: no pressure—just lovely, interesting discussions. It has motivated me for the rest of my life, and makes me interested in *all* the sciences. (It just happens I do physics better.)

I've been caught, so to speak—like someone who was given something wonderful when he was a child, and he's always looking for it again. I'm always looking, like a child, for the wonders I know I'm going to find—maybe not every time, but every once in a while. ○

Answering the BIG Question

As you do the following activities, consider the Big Question: **Why read?**

WRITE TO LEARN Richard Feynman's father taught him to be curious about the world around him. What fascinates you about the natural world? Write down a few examples in your Learner's Notebook.

PARTNER TALK With a partner, discuss how various people in your life have influenced your interests. How have they encouraged you or shared knowledge with you? What have you taught them?

Vo·cab·u·lary

physics (FIZ iks) a science that deals with matter and energy and how they interact with each other

Abuelito Who

by Sandra Cisneros

Knowing that a loved one is sick can make you feel sick inside.

Abuelito who throws coins like rain
and asks who loves him
who is dough and feathers
who is a watch and glass of water

Vo•cab•u•lary

abuelito (aw bweh LEE toh) familiar form for *abuelo,* "grandfather"
(Spanish)

whose hair is made of fur

is too sad to come downstairs today

who tells me in Spanish you are my diamond

who tells me in English you are my sky

whose little eyes are string

can't come out to play

sleeps in his little room all night and day

who used to laugh like the letter k

is sick

is a doorknob tied to a sour stick

is tired shut the door

doesn't live here anymore

is hiding underneath the bed

who talks to me inside my head

is blankets and spoons and big brown shoes

who snores up and down up and down up and down again

is the rain on the roof that falls like coins

asking who loves him

who loves him who? ○

Answering the
BIG Question

As you do the following activities, consider the Big Question:
Why read?

WRITE TO LEARN What kind of relationship does the speaker have with her abuelito? Describe in your Learner's Notebook a special relationship with a grandparent or another relative. What makes that relationship special?

PARTNER TALK Meet with another student who has read this selection. Discuss how the speaker's abuelito enriches her life. Why are relationships between people of different generations so important?

MACONA,
THE
Honest Warrior

by Barbara Winther

A courageous warrior finds friends in unusual places when he is falsely accused.

Characters

Macona

Green Parrot

Red Parrot

Luwantai

Princess

Old Soribu, *her attendant*

Chief

Two Warriors

Mosquitoes, extras

Scene 1

Setting: An Indian village in the Guianas, South America, near the Essequibo River. Upstage there is a Carib Indian house with working doorway. There is a fishing net lying on stage, beside steps. Aisle of auditorium represents river. There are two trees on opposite sides of stage steps. Several tropical plants are near backdrop.

At Rise: Jungle animal sounds are heard from offstage. Green Parrot and Red Parrot are perched in trees, squawking, flapping wings, preening, and peering through leaves. Macona is sitting on steps, mending the net. ❶

> **❶ Understanding Graphics**
> How do the photographs on these two pages help you visualize the characters and the setting?

Vo•cab•u•lary

extras (EK struz) additional characters in a play who have a small part
backdrop (BAK drop) background
preening (PREEN ing) dressing up or smoothing oneself

Macona. (*disturbed*) For the second time this week my net has been broken and my fish stolen. (*gestures and peers down audience aisle*) It must be a thief who moves silently along the Essequibo River. Is it an alligator? An angry spirit of the rain forest? Or could it be a warrior from the neighboring village (*points*) up the river? ❷

> ❷ **Setting a Purpose for Reading**
> What do you want to find out as you read this play?

Green Parrot. (*flapping wings and squawking; in high voice*) It is not an alligator, Macona, for your net was cut with a <u>machete</u>.

Red Parrot. (*also flapping wings and squawking; in <u>gravelly</u> voice*) And there is not a spirit in the Guianas who would be angry with you, for your honesty and bravery are well known.

Macona. (*rising*) Who speaks to me from the trees?

Green Parrot. I am Green Parrot.

Red Parrot. I am Red Parrot.

Green Parrot. We have magical powers.

Red Parrot. We speak when truth should be known.

Macona. Do you know who stole my fish?

Green Parrot and Red Parrot. (*together*) We know. We know.

Macona. How can I find out who it is?

Green Parrot. Leave your net in the river and hide close by. (Macona *hides.*)

Red Parrot. Again the thief comes. See him pole his boat down the river. (Macona *looks out from behind tree as* Luwantai, *wearing machete in waistband, enters at rear of auditorium, and*

Vo•cab•u•lary

machete (ma SHEH tee) a large knife used in cutting sugarcane, for hacking one's way through the jungle, and as a weapon
gravelly (GRAV uh lee) having a rough or grating sound

*comes down center aisle. He <u>pantomimes</u> poling a pirogue—
canoe—<u>stealthily</u> jumping ashore when he gets to steps.)*

Luwantai. *(seeing net)* There are some fine fish in this net. I will
take them for myself. *(He pantomimes slashing net with machete,
and then throwing fish into boat. He replaces machete in waistband
and starts to shove boat into water.)*

Macona. *(stepping out)* So, a warrior from our neighboring village
is the thief.

Luwantai. *(angrily; pointing to himself)* How dare you accuse Luwantai?

Macona. Tell me, Luwantai, are all your village warriors thieves,
or is it just those too lazy to catch their own fish, like you?

Luwantai. *(shouting)* I am not lazy. *(Parrots squawk as if laughing.)*

Macona. If you are not a thief and you are not lazy, then how did
my fish get into your pirogue?

Luwantai. *(nervously)* Well, ah, that is easy to explain. *(sees
Parrots, who are squawking, and points to them)* The Parrots
in the tree did it. They threw the fish into my boat. *(Parrots
squawk loudly in protest. Luwantai pantomimes pulling arrow
from quiver, fitting it in bow, and aiming it at tree as he speaks.)*
Those thieving birds will die by my poisoned arrows. *(Macona
pantomimes grabbing bow and arrow and <u>hurling</u> them into river.)*

Macona. *(as he does this)* I, Macona, will not let you kill these
Parrots.

Luwantai. *(angrily)* Not only do you falsely accuse me, Macona,
but you steal my bow and arrow and throw them in the river.
My village will hear about this.

Macona. *(turning away, arms folded)* I am not afraid of you,
Luwantai. You are a thief who uses <u>boastful</u> words. *(As Macona*

Vo•cab•u•lary

pantomimes (PAN toh mymz) acting out a story with bodily or facial
movements
stealthily (STELTH uh lee) slowly and secretly in action
hurling (HURL ing) throwing violently
boastful (BOHST ful) bragging

speaks, Luwantai *pantomimes shoving off pirogue, leaping into it, and then poling quickly down aisle to exit.*) I know who stole my fish, for I was hidden here and I saw you—(*whirls to point, then sees* Luwantai *exiting, and calls defiantly after him*) This time you have escaped. But I shall come after you.

Green Parrot. Forget this thief, Macona. He will not return.

Red Parrot. It would be too dangerous to follow him to his village.

Macona. (*pulling in net and throwing it off*) There is a code of honor among my people. A thief should pay with more than he takes. I must go to his village now and settle this matter. (*pantomimes pushing pirogue off steps, jumping in, and then poling down aisle to exit*) ❸

Green Parrot. (*after* Macona *exits*) There will be trouble for him.

Red Parrot. Surely the Chief of Luwantai's village will not harm Macona.

Green Parrot. Perhaps not. Perhaps he will. The minds of men work strangely.

> ❸ **Identifying Main Idea and Supporting Details**
> List the reasons that Macona gives for going to Luwantai's village.

Red Parrot. Let us fly to the neighboring village. Macona saved our lives. He may need our help. (*Parrots come out of trees, flap wings as if flying, and exit, squawking. Curtain*)

Scene 2

Setting: A neighboring village, where Luwantai's people live. House has been moved up center. One tree is at left and one is at right.

At Rise: Princess is sitting center, having her hair combed by Old Soribu, who kneels beside her. Sounds of jungle animals are heard. Macona enters at rear of auditorium and comes down aisle, pantomiming poling pirogue to steps and beaching it. Princess rises, startled, and Old Soribu stands in front of her protectively.

Macona. Do not be afraid. I will not harm you.

Old Soribu. I can tell by your headdress you come from the village down the river.

Macona. Yes. I am called Macona. (*Soribu and Princess gasp and look around for others.*)

Soribu. (*approaching him, whispering*) Leave at once, Macona. Old Soribu warns you, for I wish no man harm.

Princess. (*coming forward*) Go quickly. My father is the Chief of this village. He has vowed revenge on you.

Macona. Why?

Princess. You insulted the warrior Luwantai.

Macona. For good reason, lovely Princess. Luwantai is a lazy thief. Please believe me.

Princess. (*turning sadly away*) It does not matter if I believe you. No one else in my village will. (*turns to him*) Luwantai is my father's favorite warrior.

Soribu. (*gesturing*) The Princess is promised to him in marriage.

Macona. (*crossing to her*) It makes me sad that one whose hair shines more than a hummingbird's wing and whose eyes flash like fireflies in the dark, should marry such a man as Luwantai.

Princess. (*smiling*) Though your actions are as bold as the jaguar, your words are softer than a butterfly. Please, Macona, go while there is time. (Luwantai *and* Two Warriors *enter left, stealthily, unseen.*)

Macona. (*kneeling*) No. Now that I have met the Princess, there is even more reason to expose Luwantai's <u>deceit</u>. (*Suddenly* Luwantai *and* Warriors *leap out from hiding, whooping loudly, and jump at* Macona. Princess *and* Soribu *scream and move away, clutching each other.* Macona *fights off* Warriors *and goes after* Luwantai, *who backs away fearfully.* Warriors *scramble to feet, and one grabs* Macona's *arms while other holds his legs. They pull him back toward steps.*)

Luwantai. Tie him up. (Warriors *pantomime tying* Macona's *hands and ankles.* Luwantai *crosses to house, calling*) Great Chief! I, Luwantai, your fine warrior, have captured the treacherous Macona. (*crosses arms arrogantly*)

Chief. (*from inside house; wildly, ad lib*) Ay ya ook! Ay kai ya! (*etc. All stare at doorway. Suddenly* Chief *leaps out of house. He wears fierce-looking mask and* <u>raffia</u> *costume. He rushes about in circle, shaking costume. Finally he stops in front of house and leaps, with a* <u>yelp</u>. *Pointing to* Macona) Macona, you shall die. (*With cry of* <u>anguish</u>, Princess *rushes forward and kneels beside* Chief, *her arms raised pleadingly.*)

Princess. No, no, Father. Please give Macona a chance to prove his innocence.

Luwantai. Do not listen to her, great Chief.

Chief. Rise, my child. Why do you interfere?

Vo•cab•u•lary

deceit (duh SEET) trickery or prank
raffia (RAF ee uh) fiber of the raffia palm used for making baskets and hats
yelp (yelp) a sharp, shrill cry
anguish (ANG gwish) extreme pain or distress

Princess. (*rising*) Because I believe my father is fair enough to listen to both sides of any quarrel. (*Chief folds arms.*) Speak, Macona.

Macona. Luwantai slashed my net and stole my fish. I saw him.

Luwantai. He lies. He lies.

Macona. I speak the truth.

Chief. Hm-m-m. I believe Luwantai, but I will be fair. There will be a test. Whoever wins speaks the truth and marries my daughter.

Luwantai. (*startled*) A test? For me?

Macona. Whatever the test, I will do it.

Chief. You must each go into the forest and carve a wooden stool before morning. On one side carve a monkey's head; on the other side— my face.

Luwantai. That's easy.

Macona. I cannot do this, Chief, until I see your face.

Chief. You may not. I will not take off this mask all night, but still you must carve an exact likeness of me. (*to Princess*) Princess, do not tell Macona what I look like, or you will be a traitor to our village. (*to men*) Remember, Macona and Luwantai, carve the stool by morning or you shall die.

Princess. Father, this test is not fair. Luwantai knows what your face looks like.

Chief. Of course.

Princess. How can Macona possibly know?

Macona, the Honest Warrior

Chief. *(laughing)* He can't. *(to* Warriors*)* Cut Macona's bonds and let the trial begin. *(exits into house. Princess weeps on Soribu's shoulder. Warriors pantomime cutting Macona's bonds, then exit. Macona thoughtfully rubs wrists. Luwantai crosses right, passing Princess.)*

Luwantai. *(mockingly)* Poor Princess weeps for doomed Macona. What a pity! *(exits right, laughing)*

Princess. *(hurrying to* Macona*)* Go back to your village. Save yourself.

Macona. *(with dignity)* I am a warrior, Princess. I will not run from danger. It is not honorable. *(exits left. Lights dim to indicate passage of time. Princess and Soribu exit. Sounds of jungle animals are heard. Parrots enter, climb into tree near steps. As lights go up half, Luwantai reenters, right, carrying block of wood. It has been partially carved.)*

Luwantai. *(yawning sleepily)* The night is only half over. There is plenty of time to finish carving my stool. First I will take a nap under this tree. *(lies under tree at right and falls asleep. He remains onstage sleeping throughout following scene. Jungle animal sounds are heard. Lights go up three quarters. Macona reenters, left, carrying block of wood and knife. He pantomimes carving.)*

Macona. *(inspecting stool)* This stool is finished except for the Chief's face. What features should I carve? *(looks at sky)* Soon it will be morning. *(shakes head in despair)* It seems I have lost the Princess and my life. ❹

Green and Red Parrots. *(together)* Macona, Macona.

Macona. Who calls?

Green Parrot. *(high voice)* The magical parrots.

Red Parrot. *(gravelly voice)* You saved us from the poisoned arrows. Now we will save you.

Macona. How can you help?

Green Parrot. The Chief sleeps in his house. *(Macona looks at*

> **❹ Scanning**
> Scan to find out how the parrots plan to save Macona. Does their plan work?

house and nods.)

Red Parrot. We shall call our mosquito friends.

Green Parrot. They will enter his house—

Red Parrot. Crawl under his mask—

Green Parrot. And bite his face.

Red Parrot. Then he will throw off the mask—

Green Parrot. Run to the river—

Red Parrot. And splash cool water on his face.

Macona. Then I shall see his face.

Green Parrot. Yes, yes, look closely.

Red Parrot. But don't let him see you. (Macona *nods and hides behind tree, carrying stool.*)

Green Parrot. *(calling* shrilly*)* Gu yai ya, Mosquito, quick, quick, quick.

Red Parrot. Gu yai ya, Mosquito, squaw-aw-ka-ka-ka-ka. (*Two Mosquitoes enter, buzzing, darting, and swaying, from right. They "fly" around stage, then enter house. There is silence. Then Chief yells and runs out of house without mask. He has two red circles on his cheeks and a star on his forehead. He leans over edge of stage and pantomimes washing face in river. Macona peers out, touches his own cheeks and forehead, then smiles and nods. Meanwhile Mosquitoes reenter from house and exit. Chief rises, looks about suspiciously. Macona pulls his head out of sight.*)

Chief. *(muttering)* Pesky Mosquitoes! (*reenters house. Macona comes out of hiding, pantomimes carving.*)

Macona. *(while carving)* Thank you, Parrots.

Green Parrot. We will stay close by.

Red Parrot. We will meet you again, Macona.

Parrots. *(climbing from tree; together)* Soon, soon, soon. *(They*

Vo•cab•u•lary

shrilly (SHRIL lee) having a sharp, high-pitched sound

exit, squawking. Animal sounds are heard. Lights go up full.)

Macona. *(rising, looking at sky)* It is morning, and I am finished. *(Warriors enter, see Luwantai asleep, and hurry over to him. They pick up the block of wood, shake heads in disgust and drop it, then awaken him. Luwantai jumps up nervously, hiding his block of wood. Princess and Soribu enter and stand sadly beside house.)*

Chief. *(from inside house)* Ay ya ook! Ay kai ya! *(etc. All stare at doorway. Suddenly, Chief leaps out, in mask, as before, and rushes around shaking raffia costume. Finally he stops in front of house and leaps with a yelp.)* Bring forth the stools. *(Macona crosses to Chief and kneels, presenting stool.)* What is this? A likeness of my face. Amazing! Macona, how did you find out what I look like? *(removes mask and gestures for him to rise)*

Macona. *(rising, smiling)* To answer that question is not part of my test. *(Chief sets mask inside house.)*

Chief. *(smiling)* I meant to trick you. Instead, you have cleverly tricked me. Luwantai, where is your stool?

Luwantai. *(nervously)* Macona stole it.

Chief. What?

Luwantai. He stole it while I was ah—ah—resting.

1st Warrior. Great Chief, Luwantai is not telling the truth. He slept all night.

2nd Warrior. His stool is hidden behind his back.

Chief. *(holding out hand)* Luwantai, give me your stool. *(Luwantai regretfully hands over block.)* So, this is how well you pass my trial. A block of wood scarcely carved. *(holding stools side by side; sternly)* Which would you say is the better stool, Luwantai?

Luwantai. *(furiously, to Macona)* This is all your fault. *(whips out machete and rushes for Macona. Just as his machete is raised high in air, Parrots enter, "flying" and squawking loudly.)*

Parrots. *(shrilly; together)* Stop! Stop! *(Luwantai, startled, turns to see Parrots,* *and* Macona *grabs machete away.* Luwantai *snarls angrily, growls at everyone, and runs to exit. Those on stage move to backdrop and peer off after him.* Luwantai *shrieks in terror from offstage and reenters,* <u>pursued</u> *by angrily buzzing* Mosquitoes. *They fly about stage.* Luwantai *runs down steps and pantomimes pushing pirogue into river, leaping into it, and poling furiously up aisle, howling.* Mosquitoes *follow. Meanwhile* Chief *places stool inside house, and* Macona *puts machete into his waistband. All move forward to watch.* Luwantai *and* Mosquitoes *exit.*)

Green Parrot. (*pointing wings to river; loudly*) A thief can never rest.

Red Parrot. Luwantai will be pursued forever.

Chief. (*extending hand to* Macona) Macona (*extends other hand to* Princess) and the Princess will be married. May there always be friendship between our villages. (*All cheer as jungle animal sounds are heard and curtain closes.*)

The End ○

Answering the BIG Question

When you do the following activities, consider the Big Question:
Why read?

WRITE TO LEARN The friendship between the parrots and Macona is very important in this play. In your Learner's Notebook, write about a time when you depended on a friend for help. How did it affect your relationship?

LITERATURE GROUPS In a small group, discuss the lies that Luwantai tells. Talk about how telling one lie can easily lead to another until a person is caught in a web of lies—as Luwantai was.

Vo•cab•u•lary

pursued (pur SOOD) followed in order to defeat

What brings out the best in you?

Sometimes you feel as if you're sitting on top of the world. It could be an event with friends or family or a job well done that makes you feel this way. Or it could be just figuring something out for yourself. As you read the following selections, think about the answer to the question: **What brings out the best in you?**

Key Reading Skills

As you read the selections in this unit, apply these reading skills.

- **Connecting** Think about what you are reading and how it relates to your own life and to other things you've read.
- **Questioning** As you read, stop from time to time and ask yourself some questions about the text. Questioning will help you decide what is important in the selection.
- **Predicting** Take an educated guess about what will happen in a selection or what it will be about.
- **Activating Prior Knowledge** Use information you already know to help you better understand what you are reading.

THE BLUE DARTER

by Judith Logan Lehne

Sometimes the only way to win is by doing the right thing.

I stood in a corner of the dugout, making circles in the dirt with my shoe, just listening.

"We *gave* them the game," Lyle said. His hair and his "Team Captain" shirt were soaked with sweat. "We played terrible."

Paul nodded and pointed his finger at Julio. "You call yourself a pitcher? You practically threw the ball right at their bats!"

"Everybody has a bad day," I said to Lyle. "Why didn't you put Lindsay in? Her Blue Darter pitch was just what we needed today." Lindsay looked over at me, and her eyes seemed to say thanks.

"Get real, Jonathan," Lyle said, moving a huge wad of gum inside his cheek. "It's bad enough I let you talk us into having a girl on the team. The Orioles would've laughed us off the field if we had let her pitch."

Lindsay pulled off her cap and shook out her long ponytail. "The score was 18 to 6, Lyle!" she said. "The Orioles got their laughs anyway."

"Well, the Cubs won't be laughing tomorrow," Lyle said. He grabbed his mitt. "Let's practice!"

Everyone <u>tromped</u> to the field.

"Jonathan," Paul said, "you're our best hitter. Tell us your secret."

"Natural talent," I said, shrugging. I felt Lindsay's eyes on me. I knew what she wanted me to tell them. I owed my batting success to her—and the hours of practice with her grandfather. He's the one who taught her the Blue Darter. I never got the hang of it, but Lindsay could whistle the ball off her fingers and make it curve crazily when I was in mid-swing. It was because of Lindsay's Blue Darter that I was a good batter. But I couldn't tell the guys that. I just couldn't.

Walking home, Lindsay was silent. When we reached her house, she turned and <u>glared</u>.

"You could have told them, Jonathan," she said between clenched teeth. "Maybe they'd have let me pitch tomorrow." ❶

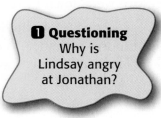

❶ Questioning
Why is Lindsay angry at Jonathan?

I glared back. "You want me to make a fool of myself? When you're not around, they always tease me. If they knew you helped my batting . . . "

She looked as though she might cry, but I kept yelling. "I got you on this team. Isn't that enough?"

"This isn't about *baseball*," she said. Her ponytail whipped across her face as she stomped away.

Vo•cab•u•lary

tromped (trawmpt) walked by stamping feet on the ground
glared (glaird) looked angrily

All night I kept hearing Lindsay saying, "This isn't about baseball." What did she mean?

Before the game with the Cubs, I apologized to her. "It's okay," she said. "I guess it's not easy having a girl for a best friend."

Listening to Lyle, the guys squirmed on the bench. Lindsay leaned against the dugout wall.

"Show 'em our best! No errors," Lyle said, blowing bubbles between words. "Julio, you pitch."

I looked at Lindsay, but I kept quiet.

We were first at bat. The Cubs' pitcher was good, but not great. When I stepped to the plate, Lyle was on third and Paul was on first. I looked at the dugout. Lindsay shouted, "Whack it!" My hands felt clammy.

"Strike one!" the umpire shouted. I hadn't even swung at it.

"Concentrate," I said to myself. The ball came toward the plate, and I swung. *Crack!* I raced to first . . . second . . . third . . . home!

After the back-slapping cheers, the game took a downward turn. The Cubs' not-so-great pitcher got better, and our hitting got worse. Julio was still in a pitching slump. By the fifth inning, we were down by seven runs.

As we took the field, I grabbed Lyle's arm. "Give Lindsay a chance," I said. The team stopped to listen. Lindsay stayed in the dugout, watching. ❷

❷ **Connecting**
Think of a time when you stood up for a friend. How did it make you feel?

"No girl pitchers," Lyle snarled. "Especially not your *girlfriend*."

"She's not my—" I began. I looked at Lindsay. This isn't about baseball, she'd said.

"She is my girl *friend*," I said. Someone snickered. "She's a girl, and she's my friend." I put my face close to Lyle's. "And when you see her Blue Darter pitch, you will know she's this *team's* friend, too."

"Let her pitch," Julio said.

Talking all at once, the guys nudged Lyle. "Let's see her Blue Darter!"

Lyle called Lindsay from the dugout. "You'd better be good," he said.

Lindsay stepped to the mound. "Come on, Lindsay," I cheered. "Show 'em your stuff."

She kicked dirt around, looking shy and not at all like a pitcher. The guys exchanged glares. Just wait, I wanted to tell them. They didn't have to wait long. She bent forward, threw her arm back, and whipped the ball off her fingers. It flew like an arrow until it was nearly over the plate, then it veered to the left.

"Strike one!" the umpire called.

Lindsay grinned at me and continued to hurl the Blue Darter at lightning speed, just as her grandfather had taught her. The Cubs never even scored another run.

We lost, but the Cubs weren't laughing.

Lyle came into the dugout and shook Lindsay's hand. He swallowed hard. "You're a terrific pitcher," he said. He turned to me. "And you've got a great best friend."

"I know," I said, looking at Lindsay. "True blue." ○

Answering the BIG Question

As you do the following activities, consider the Big Question:
What brings out the best in you?

WRITE TO LEARN Think about why Jonathan finally stood up for Lindsay. What did she teach him about friendship? Jot down your thoughts in your Learner's Notebook.

PARTNER TALK With a partner, discuss why Lyle finally agreed to let Lindsay pitch. What did he learn from her performance? What did the team learn from the whole experience?

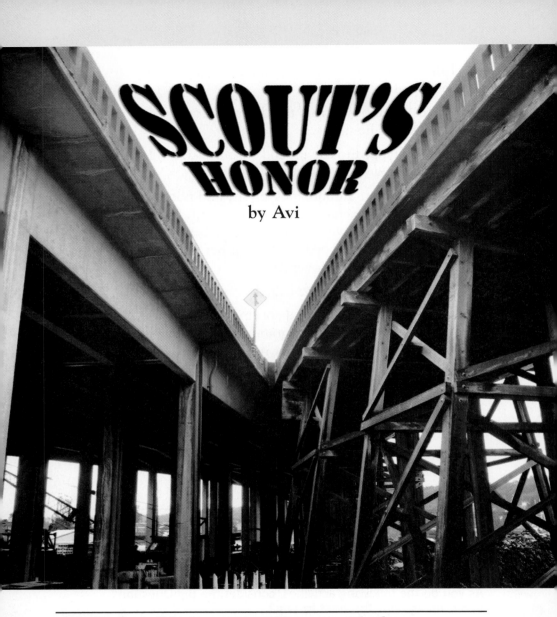

SCOUT'S HONOR

by Avi

How hard can it be to camp outside on a patch of grass across the George Washington Bridge?

Back in 1946, when I was nine, I worried that I wasn't tough enough. That's why I became a Boy Scout. Scouting, I thought, would make a man of me. It didn't take long to reach

Tenderfoot rank. You got that for joining. To move up to Second Class, however, you had to meet three requirements. Scout Spirit and Scout Participation had been cinchy. The third requirement, Scout Craft, meant I had to go on an overnight hike in the *country*. In other words, I had to leave Brooklyn, on my own, for the first time in my life. ❶

Since I grew up in Brooklyn in the 1940s, the only grass I knew was in Ebbets Field where the Dodgers played. Otherwise, my world was made of slate pavements, streets of <u>asphalt</u> (or cobblestone), and skies full of tall buildings. The only thing "country" was a puny pin oak tree at our curb, which was noticed, mostly, by dogs.

> ❶ **Connecting**
> Think of a time when you faced a brand-new experience. How did you feel?

I asked Scoutmaster Brenkman where I could find some country. Now, whenever I saw Mr. Brenkman, who was a church pastor, he was dressed either in church black or Scout khaki. When he wore black, he'd warn us against hellfire. When he wore khaki, he'd teach us how to build fires.

"Country," Scoutmaster Brenkman said in answer to my question, "is anywhere that has lots of trees and is not in the city. Many boys camp in the Palisades."

"Where's that?"

"Just north of the city. It's a park in Jersey."

"Isn't that a zillion miles from here?"

"Take the subway to the George Washington Bridge, then hike across."

I thought for a moment, then asked, "How do I prove I went?"

Mr. Brenkman looked deeply shocked. "You wouldn't *lie*, would you? What about Scout's honor?"

"Yes, sir," I replied <u>meekly</u>.

Vo•cab•u•lary

asphalt (AS fawlt) type of pavement
meekly (MEEK lee) in a way that suggests being shy

My two best friends were Philip Hossfender, whom we nicknamed Horse, and Richard Macht, called Max because we were not great spellers. They were also Scouts, Tenderfoots like me.

Horse was a skinny little kid about half my size whose way of arguing was to ball up his fist and say, "Are you saying . . . ?" in a threatening tone.

Max was on the pudgy side, but he could talk his way out of a locked room. More importantly, he always seemed to have pocket money, which gave his talk real power.

I wasn't sure why, but being best friends meant we were rivals too. One of the reasons for my wanting to be tougher was a feeling that Horse was a lot tougher than I was, and that Max was a little tougher.

"I'm going camping in the Palisades next weekend," I casually informed them.

"How come?" Max challenged.

"Scout Craft," I replied.

"Oh, *that*," Horse said with a shrug.

"Look," I said, "I don't know about you, but I don't intend to be a Tenderfoot all my life. Anyway, doing stuff in the city is for sissies. Scouting is real camping. Besides, I like roughing it."

"You saying I don't?" Horse snapped.

"I'm not saying nothing," I said.

They considered my idea. Finally, Horse said, "Yeah, well, I was going to do that, but I didn't think you guys were ready for it."

"I've been ready for *years*," Max protested.

"Then we're going, right?" I said.

They looked around at me. "If you can do it, I can do it," Max said.

"Yeah," Horse said thoughtfully.

The way they agreed made me nervous. Now I really was going to have to be tough.

We informed our folks that we were going camping overnight (which was true) and that the Scoutmaster was going with us—which was a lie. We did remember what Mr. Brenkman said about honesty, but we were baseball fans too, and since we were prepared to follow Scout law—being loyal, helpful, friendly, courteous, kind, obedient, cheerful, thrifty, brave, clean, *and* reverent—we figured a .900 batting average was not bad.

So Saturday morning we met at the High Street subway station. I got there first. Stuffed in my dad's army surplus knapsack was a blanket, a pillow, and a paper bag with three white-bread peanut butter-and-jelly sandwiches—that is, lunch, supper, and Sunday breakfast. My pockets were full of stick matches. I had an old flashlight, and since I lived by the Scout motto—Be Prepared—I had brought along an umbrella. Finally, being a serious reader, I had the latest Marvel Family comics.

Horse arrived next, his arms barely managing to hold on to a mattress that seemed twice his size. As for food, he had four cans of beans jammed into his pockets.

Max came last. He was lugging a new knapsack that contained a cast-iron frying pan, a packet of hot dogs, and a box of saltine crackers—plus two bottles. One bottle was mustard, the other, celery soda. He also had a bag of Tootsie Rolls and a shiny hatchet. "To build a lean-to," he explained.

Max's prize possession, however, was an official Scout compass. "It's really swell," he told us. "You can't ever get lost with it. Got it at the Scout store." ❷

"I hate that place," Horse informed us. "It's all new. Nothing real."

"This compass is real," Max retorted.

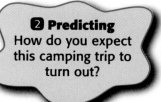

❷ **Predicting**
How do you expect this camping trip to turn out?

"Points north all the time. You can get cheaper ones, but they point all different directions."

"What's so great about the north?" Horse said.

"That's always the way to go," Max insisted.

"Says who?" I demanded.

"Mr. Brenkman, dummy," Horse cried. "Anyway, there's always an arrow on maps pointing the way north."

"Cowboys live out west," I reminded them. They didn't care.

On the subway platform, we realized we did not know which station we were heading for. To find out, we studied the system map, which looked like a noodle factory hit by a bomb. The place we wanted to go (north) was at the top of the map, so I had to hoist Horse onto my shoulders for a closer look. Since he refused to let go of his mattress—or the tin cans in his pockets—it wasn't easy. I asked him—in a kindly fashion—to put the mattress down.

No sooner did he find the station—168th Street—than our train arrived. We rushed on, only to have Horse scream, "My mattress!" He had left it on the platform. Just before the doors shut, he and I leaped off. Max, however, remained on the train. Helplessly, we watched as his horror-stricken face slid away from us. "Wait at the next station!" I bellowed. "Don't move!"

The next train took forever to come. Then it took even longer to get to the next stop. There was Max. All around him— like fake snow in a glass ball—were crumbs. He'd been so nervous he had eaten all his crackers.

"Didn't that make you thirsty?"

"I drank my soda."

I noticed streaks down his cheeks. Horse noticed them too. "You been crying?" he asked.

"Naw," Max said. "There was this water dripping from the tunnel roof. But, you said don't move, right? Well, I was just being obedient."

By the time we got on the next train—with all our possessions—we had been traveling for an hour. But we had managed to go only one stop.

During the ride, I got hungry. I pulled out one of my sandwiches. With the jelly soaked through the bread, it looked like a limp scab.

Horse, envious, complained he was getting hungry.

"Eat some of your canned beans," I suggested.

He got out one can without ripping his pocket too badly. Then his face took on a mournful look.

"What's the matter?" I asked.

"Forgot to bring a can opener."

Max said, "In the old days, people opened cans with their teeth."

"You saying my teeth aren't strong?"

"I'm just talking about history!"

"You saying I don't know history?"

Always kind, I plopped half my sandwich into Horse's hand. He squashed it into his mouth and was quiet for the next fifteen minutes. It proved something I'd always believed: The best way to stop arguments is to get people to eat peanut butter sandwiches. They can't talk.

Then we became so absorbed in our Marvel Family comics we missed our station. We got to it only by coming back the other way. When we reached street level, the sky was dark.

"I knew it," Max announced. "It's going to rain."

"Don't worry," Horse said. "New Jersey is a whole other state. It probably won't be raining there."

"I brought an umbrella," I said smugly, though I wanted it to sound helpful.

As we marched down 168th Street, heading for the George Washington Bridge, we looked like European war <u>refugees</u>. Every few paces, Horse cried, "Hold it!" and adjusted his arms around his mattress. Each time we paused, Max pulled out his compass, peered at it, then announced, "Heading north!"

I said, "The bridge goes from east to west."

"Maybe the bridge does," Max insisted with a show of his compass, "but guaranteed, *we* are going north."

About then, the heel of my left foot, encased in a heavy rubber boot over an earth-crushing Buster Brown shoe, started to get sore. Things weren't going as I had hoped. Cheerfully, I tried to ignore the pain.

The closer we drew to the bridge, the more <u>immense</u> it seemed. And the clouds had become so thick, you couldn't see the top or the far side.

Max eyed the bridge with deep suspicion. "I'm not so sure we should go," he said.

"Why?"

"Maybe it doesn't have another side."

We looked at him.

"No, seriously," Max explained, "they could have taken the Jersey side away, you know, for repairs."

"Cars are going across," I pointed out.

"They could be dropping off," he suggested.

"You would hear them splash," Horse argued.

"I'm going," I said. Trying to look brave, I started off on my

---

Vo•cab•u•lary

refugees (ref yoo JEEZ) people who leave one country for another because of war or to save their lives
immense (ih MENS) extremely big

own. My bravery didn't last long. The walkway was narrow. When I looked down, I saw only fog. I could feel the bridge tremble and sway. It wasn't long before I was convinced the bridge was about to collapse. ❸ Then a ray of hope struck me: Maybe the other guys had chickened out. If they had, I could quit because of *them*. I glanced back. My heart sank. They were coming.

❸ **Questioning**
Why is crossing the bridge such a scary experience?

After they caught up, Horse looked me in the eye and said, "If this bridge falls, I'm going to kill you."

A quarter of a mile farther across, I gazed around. We were completely fogged in.

"I think we're lost," I announced.

"What do we do?" Horse whispered. His voice was jagged with panic. That made me feel better.

"Don't worry," Max said. "I've got my compass." He pulled it out. "North is that way," he said, pointing in the direction we had been going.

Horse said, "You sure?"

"A Scout compass never lies," Max insisted.

"*We* lied," I reminded him.

"Yeah, but this is an *official* Scout compass," Max returned loyally.

"Come on," Max said and marched forward. Horse and I followed. In moments, we crossed a metal bar on the walkway. On one side, a sign proclaimed: NEW YORK; on the other side, it said: NEW JERSEY.

"Holy smoke," Horse said with <u>reverence</u> as he straddled the bar. "Talk about being tough. We're in two states at the same time."

It began to rain. Max said, "Maybe it'll keep us clean."

"You saying I'm not clean?" Horse shot back.

Ever friendly, I put up my umbrella.

We went on—Max on one side, Horse on the other, me in the middle—trying to avoid the growing puddles. After a while, Max said, "Would you move the umbrella? Rain is coming down my neck."

"We're supposed to be roughing it," I said.

"Being in the middle isn't roughing it," Horse reminded me.

I folded the umbrella so we all could get soaked equally. **4**

"Hey!" I cried. "Look!" Staring up ahead, I could make out tollbooths and the dim outlines of buildings.

"Last one off the bridge is a rotten egg!" Horse shouted and began to run. The next second, he tripped and took off like an F-36 fighter plane. Unfortunately, he landed like a Hell-cat dive-bomber as his mattress unspooled before him and then slammed into a big puddle.

Max and I ran to help. Horse was damp. His mattress was soaked. When he tried to roll it up, water cascaded like Niagara Falls.

"Better leave it," Max said.

4 Questioning
How does the incident with the umbrella add to your understanding of the narrator's personality?

George Washington Bridge →

Vo•cab•u•lary

reverence (REV ur uns) a feeling of respect, love, and admiration

"It's what I sleep on at home," Horse said as he slung the soaking, dripping mass over his shoulder.

When we got off the bridge, we were in a small plaza. To the left was the roadway, full of roaming cars. In front of us, aside from the highway, there was nothing but buildings. Only to the right were there trees.

"North is that way," Max said, pointing toward the trees. We set off.

"How come you're limping?" Horse asked me. My foot *was* killing me. All I said, though, was, "How come you keep rubbing your arm?"

"I'm keeping the blood moving."

We approached the grove of trees. "Wow," Horse exclaimed. "Country." But as we drew closer, what we found were discarded cans, bottles, and newspapers—plus an old mattress spring.

"Hey," Max cried, sounding relieved, "this is just like Brooklyn."

I said, "Let's find a decent place, make camp, and eat."

It was hard to find a campsite that didn't have junk. The growing dark didn't help. We had to settle for the place that had the least amount of garbage.

Max said, "If we build a lean-to, it'll keep us out of the rain." He and Horse went a short distance with the hatchet.

Seeing a tree they wanted, Max whacked at it. The hatchet bounced right out of his hand. There was not even a dent in the tree. Horse retrieved the hatchet and checked the blade. "Dull," he said.

"Think I'm going to carry something sharp and cut myself?" Max protested. They contented themselves with picking up branches.

I went in search of firewood, but everything was wet. When I finally gathered some twigs and tried to light them, the only thing that burned was my fingers.

Meanwhile, Horse and Max used their branches to build a

lean-to directly over me. After many collapses—which didn't help my work—they finally got the branches to stand in a shaky sort of way.

"Uh-oh," Horse said. "We forgot to bring something for a cover."

Max eyed me. "Didn't you say you brought a blanket?"

"No way!" I cried.

"All in favor of using the blanket!"

Horse and Max both cried, "Aye."

Only after I built up a mound of partially burned match sticks and lit *them*, did I get the fire going. It proved that where there's smoke there doesn't have to be much fire. The guys meanwhile draped my blanket over their branch construction. It collapsed twice.

About an hour after our arrival, the three of us were gathered inside the tiny space. There was a small fire, but more light came from my flickering flashlight.

"No more rain," Horse said with pride.

"Just smoke," I said, rubbing my stinging eyes.

"We need a vent hole," Horse pointed out.

"I could cut it with the hatchet," Max said.

"It's my mother's favorite blanket."

"And you took it?" Max said.

I nodded.

"You *are* tough," Horse said.

Besides having too much smoke in our eyes and being wet, tired, and in pain, we were starving. I almost said something about giving up, but as far as I could see, the other guys were still tough. **5**

5 Predicting
Do you think the boys will give up or manage to tough it out?

Max put his frying pan atop my <u>smoldering</u> smoke. After dumping in the entire contents of his mustard bottle, he threw in the franks. Meanwhile, I bolted down my last sandwich.

"What am I going to eat?" Horse suddenly said.

"Your beans," I reminded him.

Max offered up his hatchet. "Here. Just chop off the top end of the can."

"Oh, right," Horse said. He selected a can, set it in front of him, levered himself onto his knees, then swung down—hard.

Vo•cab•u•lary

smoldering (SMOHL duh ring) burning without a flame

There was an explosion. For a stunned moment, we just sat there, hands, face, and clothing dripping with beans.

Suddenly Max shouted, "Food Fight! Food Fight!" and began to paw the stuff off and fling it around.

Having a food fight in a cafeteria is one thing. Having one in the middle of a soaking wet lean-to with cold beans during a dark, wet New Jersey night is another. In seconds, the lean-to was down, the fire kicked over, and Max's frankfurters dumped on the ground.

"The food!" Max screamed, and began to snatch up the franks. Coated with mustard, dirt, grass, and leaves, they looked positively prehistoric. Still, we wiped the franks clean on our pants then ate them—the franks that is. Afterward, we picked beans off each other's clothes—the way monkeys help friends get rid of lice.

For dessert, Max shared some Tootsie Rolls. After Horse swallowed his sixteenth piece, he announced, "I don't feel so good."

The thought of his getting sick was too much. "Let's go home," I said, ashamed to look at the others. To my surprise—and relief—nobody objected.

Wet and cold, our way lit by my fast-fading flashlight, we gathered our belongings—most of them, anyway. As we made our way back over the bridge, gusts of windblown rain pummeled us until I felt like a used-up punching bag. By the time we got to the subway station, my legs were melting fast. The other guys looked bad too. Other riders moved away from us. One of them murmured, "Juvenile delinquents." To cheer us up, I got out my comic books, but they had congealed into a lump of red, white, and blue pulp.

With the subways running slow, it took hours to get home.

Vo·cab·u·lary

juvenile delinquents (JOO vuh nyl duh LINK wunts) young kids who look like they're up to no good
pulp (pulp) a soupy mix of wet paper

When we emerged from the High Street Station, it was close to midnight.

Before we split up to go to our own homes, we just stood there on a street corner, embarrassed, trying to figure out how to end the day gracefully. I was the one who said, "Okay, I admit it. I'm not as tough as you guys. I gave up first."

Max shook his head. "Naw. I wanted to quit, but I wasn't tough enough to do it." He looked to Horse.

Horse made a fist. "You saying I'm the one who's tough?" he demanded. "I hate roughing it!"

"Me too," I said quickly.

"Same for me," Max said.

Horse said, "Only thing is, we just have to promise not to tell Mr. Brenkman."

Grinning with relief, we <u>simultaneously</u> clasped hands. "No matter what," Max reminded us.

To which I added, "Scout's Honor." **6** ○

> **6 Questioning**
> What is funny about what the narrator says here?

Answering the BIG Question

As you do the following activities, consider the Big Question:
What brings out the best in you?

WRITE TO LEARN Think about a time when you pushed yourself to do something you really didn't want to do. Why did you think you had to do it? Write about the experience in your Learner's Notebook.

PARTNER TALK Meet with another student who has read this short story. Talk about what really motivated the boys to go camping. Why was it so hard for them to admit that they wanted to go home?

Vo·cab·u·lary

simultaneously (sy mul TAY nee us lee) at the same time

Tracy McGrady

by Denise Henry

Screaming fans and championship dreams are all in a day's work for a basketball superstar.

Tracy McGrady is ready for takeoff. He is a star shooting guard on the Houston Rockets basketball team. Where is Tracy going? This NBA season, Tracy wants to soar all the way to the top and win the championship.

Big Shoes, Big Dreams

Tracy, 26, was born in Bartow, Florida. As a kid, he loved sports. During his sophomore year in high school, Tracy grew to be a very tall young man.

"My mom and my dad are really not that tall," he tells *Action*. "I think both of them are 5'11". I was a little surprised by my growth spurt."

Today, Tracy is 6'8". But *no one* is surprised that he's a <u>magnificent</u> basketball player. Last year, Tracy's team almost made it to the NBA finals. The Rockets lost against the Dallas Mavericks. But they played well as a team. One of Tracy's teammates is Yao Ming. Yao is 7'5".

"Yao and I realized how dangerous we are when we play together. We bring out the best in one another," Tracy says. ❶

Together, these big men are working hard to make their NBA dreams come true.

> ❶ **Activating Prior Knowledge**
> What else do you know about Tracy McGrady and Yao Ming?

T-Mac's Mission

Tracy's nickname is T-Mac. T-Mac comes alive when he's on the basketball court.

"This is what I love to do," he says. "I just go out and try to get as much out of myself as I possibly can before my career is done."

Tracy plays in an <u>auditorium</u> full of fans who cheer and foes who boo him. Both reactions make Tracy work even harder to succeed.

"The <u>ultimate</u> goal for me is to win a championship," he says. "I work on my game daily. I want to be known as a great player in this league and a great winner."

Vo•cab•u•lary

magnificent (mag NIF ih sint) excellent
auditorium (aw di TOR ee um) a large gathering place for an audience
ultimate (UL tuh mit) greatest; highest

"Never Give Up"

Tracy knows that he can't win every game. But he can go out each night and play his hardest. Even when Tracy makes bad plays on the court, he never gives up.

"We all make mistakes," he tells *Action*. "I learn from my mistakes and move on."

Tracy knows this attitude works off the court as well.

"Never give up," Tracy says. "If you fail, so be it. Everybody fails. Bounce back and work 10 times as hard as you did before. Hard work always pays off." ○

Answering the BIG Question

As you do the following activities, consider the Big Question:
What brings out the best in you?

WRITE TO LEARN Think about how Tracy looks at life both on and off the basketball court. Write a brief entry in your Learner's Notebook describing Tracy's outlook on life.

LITERATURE GROUPS Meet with two or three others who have read this article. Discuss Tracy's "never give up" attitude. Then talk about times when hard work has paid off in your lives.

THE CALAMITY KIDS IN

WEAKNESS OF WILL!

by Jerzy Drozd and Sara Turner

Being special can mean many different things.

"THERE WAS THE TIME WHEN SUN HAD FOUND THIS PUZZLE-BOX.

"APPARENTLY, SATURNIANS ARE REALLY GOOD WITH PUZZLES.

"IT TOOK HER A COUPLE OF DAYS...

KLAK!

"BUT SHE FIGURED IT OUT.

"THIS ENTITY SUDDENLY CAME OUT OF THE BOX.

WHOOSH!

HOW'S IT GOIN'?

I'M FRANK.

"I GUESS ITS NAME WAS FRANK.

"SUN ASSUMED HE WAS SOME KIND OF GENIE...

SATURNIANS DON'T TYPICALLY DESIRE WISHES, BUT FOR CURIOSITY'S SAKE...

ZIP!

1 PONY
2 ROCKET SHIP
3. DINOSAUR
4 KIDS MAKE-UP KIT
5. HELMET CRAP
6. PRACTICE AMMUNITION
7. MOON BOOTS
8. UNICORN
9. ROLLER SKATES
10. BIKE

HERE'S MY LIST!

SATURN? YOU'RE A WEIRD KID.

WEIRD?

"BUT THERE WAS SOMETHING FRANK HAD ON HIS MIND OTHER THAN GRANTING WISHES...

LATER, YOU!

KRAK!

"NAMELY, CAUSING TROUBLE.

101

WRITE TO LEARN
Will's special talent is bringing out the best in his friends. In your Learner's Notebook, write about one of your special talents or qualities.

end.

RACING STRIPES

What happens when a zebra thinks he's a different animal?

Malcolm in the Middle star Frankie Muniz really mouths off in the movie Racing Stripes! Frankie performs the voice of Stripes, who believes that he's a racehorse. There's just one problem—he's a zebra!

Frankie took a break from the set of Malcolm to chat with NG (National Geographic) KIDS about the movie:

NGK: What did you like best about playing a zebra?

FM: Not many people can say they've done it! It's cool to hear my voice coming out of Stripes' mouth.

NGK: Tell us the secret to making a live zebra talk.

FM: Computer artists filmed my mouth as I read Stripes' lines, then they animated the zebra's mouth so it moved like mine.

NGK: What should kids do when they feel like an underdog like Stripes? **❶**

FM: As long as you're happy with what you're doing, don't worry about what other people think. Just have fun and be yourself. ○

> **❶ Connecting**
> Have you ever felt like an underdog?

Answering the BIG Question

As you do the following activities, consider the Big Question:
What brings out the best in you?

WRITE TO LEARN Think about Frankie's advice to kids who feel like underdogs. Write a brief entry in your Learner's Notebook describing how you might apply this advice to your own life.

PARTNER TALK Join with a partner who has read "Racing Stripes." Write a skit in which a reporter interviews the zebra about his desire to race. You may perform your skit for the class.

teacher? doctor? lawyer? artist?
scientist? gardener? lifeguard?
house painter? soldier? waiter?
arch   musician? realtor?
pilo   ? psychiatri
diet

Experts, Incorporated

by Sarah Weeks

Sometimes the answer to your problems is right in front of you.

There are three things in this world I can't stand—
cucumber salad, wool sweaters, and creative writing. Cucumbers
make me burp and wool makes me itch, but if you gave me a
choice, I would rather burp and itch at the same time than have
to write something creative.

"You finished your essay, right, Rodd-o?" my friend Lucas
asked me as we walked toward school together early one morning.

I hesitated. Lucas is my best friend and we always shoot
straight with each other.

"Yeah, I finished," I said.

"Phew, that's a relief," he said. "If you hadn't, I would have to
kill you, you know."

"Yeah, I know," I said.

The problem began on the first day of the school year when our humanities teacher, Mrs. Greenberg, promised that if nobody got an F in her class all semester she would give us a pizza party.

"Just remember," she'd laughed, "there are no F's in *pizza*."

Here it was, the last week of the semester and I was about to earn not just an F, but the F that would ruin everything. Because, you see, I hadn't done the assignment. Not one word of it.

As we rounded the corner and headed up the block toward school, Jeremy and Russell, two friends from our class, caught up with us.

"You guys did the assignment, right?" Russell asked us.

"Yes," Lucas answered for us both. "How about you?"

"Of course," said Jeremy. "What do we look like, idiots? I can taste that pepperoni already. Last year's class got the party and somebody told me she let them have all the soda they wanted too."

When I get nervous, I sometimes get <u>hives</u> on my neck, and I could feel one beginning to prickle up under my collar. ❶

❶ **Questioning**
Ask yourself why Rodd-o is so nervous.

"What profession did you pick?" Lucas asked.

"Doctor," Jeremy said. "'Cause they get to save people and stuff."

"I picked truck driver," said Russell. "They get to travel and eat at diners. I love diners, but my mom says they're too greasy, so we never get to go. What about you, Lucas?"

"Star pitcher for the New York Yankees," he said. "Man, can you imagine getting paid to play baseball?"

The assignment had been to write an essay about what you want to be when you grow up. Sounds easy enough, unless you're

---

Vo•cab•u•lary

hives (hyvz) a kind of itchy rash

like me and have no idea what you want to be, and no matter how hard you try, you can't think of even one thing that feels the least bit right.

"I bet all the girls are going to say they want to be teachers 'cause they know Mrs. Greenberg will eat that up with a spoon," Russell said with disgust.

"Yeah, probably," Lucas agreed. "So, what did you pick, Rodd-o?" he asked, turning to me.

We were just starting up the steps of the school, when a familiar cry went up from the playground.

"Hey look, everybody! There goes Mucus! Hey, Mucus!"

Lucas blushed and hung his head as we walked up the steps and into the building. It happens to him all the time, poor guy. He has one of the worst names. Not only does *Lucas* rhyme with *mucus*, but even if you shorten it to *Luke*, you're still in trouble because then it rhymes with *puke*. He's been tortured his whole life on account of that name. ❷

❷ Connecting
Can you imagine how it feels to get teased all the time?

Having a bad name is something Lucas and I have in common and probably part of the reason we became friends all the way back on the first day of kindergarten. My name is Rodney Curtain. My parents and my teachers call me Rod, my friends call me Rodd-o, and my sister, who's only two, calls me Rah-rah. Rodney Curtain may not be the greatest name in the world, but frontward like that it's not so bad. The thing is, at school when they call out your name for attendance they say it backward. Lucas Bromberg becomes Bromberg, Lucas. Samantha Smith becomes Smith, Samantha.

Unfortunately, I become Curtain, Rod. That's bad.

As we made our way down the hall to homeroom, I felt sorry for Lucas on account of the teasing, but secretly I was relieved that he'd forgotten about the question he'd asked me. How was he going to take it when he found out I hadn't done the assignment?

After she took attendance, Mrs. Greenberg—we have her for homeroom as well as humanities—announced that she would be collecting our papers after lunch. There was still hope left. All I had to do was come up with an idea between now and then, scribble it down in time to hand it in with the others, and maybe I wouldn't have to ruin the party after all. The problem was, I still didn't have any ideas.

"What do I want to be?" I asked myself. "Come on, Curtain, think."

I thought about it during math, history, and science lab, but with lunchtime only minutes away, my mind was still a complete blank. The only thing I could think of that I wanted to be was someone else. Someone who had written the stupid essay already.

As I looked around the room desperately hoping to find some inspiration somewhere, I asked myself, "Do I want to be a scientist? Do I want to fix clocks? Write books? Build desks? Make pencils?" No, no, no. And then suddenly without warning, everything shifted into slow motion as my eyes came to rest on the face of the girl sitting in the second seat in the third row from the left. That's when it hit me. I knew what I wanted to be. What the world needed me to be.

When the bell for lunch rang, I didn't join the others in the cafeteria.

Instead I took out my notebook and began to write. When the fifth-period bell rang, I was already in my seat in Mrs. Greenberg's room with a stack of four handwritten sheets of paper in front of me and a huge grin on my face.

"Why are you sitting there smiling like a dork?" Lucas asked as he slid into the seat next to me. "And where were you at lunch anyway? And another thing, you never answered my question from before, what did you choose as your profession?"

"Name expert," I told him happily. "That's definitely what I want to be, a name expert."

Experts, Incorporated

"A name expert? Whoever heard of that?" he said.

"Nobody. It hasn't been invented yet. But I'm going to be the first one," I told him.

"Oh, yeah? And what exactly are you going to do?" he asked me.

"I'm going to advise people about what not to name their kids." ❸

"No offense, but that is so dumb. Why would anybody pay you to tell them what not to name their kid?" he asked.

❸ **Questioning**
What inspired Rod to think up this job?

"Because I'm an expert," I said.

"Says who?" he said.

"What's your name?"

"What do you mean, what's my name? You know my name, fish-for-brains." Lucas snorted.

"Come on, just answer the question. What's your name?"

"Lucas," he said.

"And what do all the kids call you?"

He hesitated uncomfortably for a second before answering.

"Mucus," he said quietly.

"Exactly," I said. "See? If I had been around when your parents were deciding what to name you, I could have warned them that every name needs to be checked for bad rhymes. A kid named Leo is gonna end up getting called B.O. Anybody named Gabby is gonna get called Flabby. It doesn't take a rocket scientist to figure that out. Your name is particularly bad, because it's a double whammy."

"Tell me about it," said Lucas, shaking his head sadly.

"The way I see it, a name

expert should be hired every time a baby gets born, to protect it from being <u>saddled</u> with a name that could ruin its life," I went on.

"How much do you think you'll get paid?" he asked.

"A lot. Parents pay a bundle for braces to straighten their kids' teeth. Don't you think they'd shell out even more to save their kids from being humiliated in school?"

"Here's a question for you—do you think there's any way a name expert could figure out whether a name is going to fit when the kid gets older?" Lucas asked me.

"What do you mean?" I said.

"Well, for instance, you know how Melody Adams is <u>tone-deaf</u>?"

"Yeah, she sings like a moose," I said.

"If her parents had known she was going to be unmusical, maybe they wouldn't have given her a musical name like Melody."

"Maybe they would have named her Moose," I said.

We both laughed.

"I suppose a name expert could be trained to look carefully at the parents for signs of what's to come," I said. "Like for instance, if there's a history of baldness in a family, it's probably not a very good idea to use the name Harry."

"Yeah, or like if the parents have big noses, they shouldn't name their kid Honker," said Lucas.

"Who names their kid Honker?" I said. "That's not even a real name."

"Oh, and Curtain Rod is?"

I punched him in the arm, but not too hard because like I said, we're best friends.

Vo•cab•u•lary

saddled (SAD uld) stuck
tone-deaf (TOHN def) unable to hear differences in musical notes

"Hyphenated names would have to be looked at very carefully too, don't you think?" Lucas said. "Like Jessica's, for instance."

"Exactly," I said. "She's the one I was looking at in science lab when this whole idea came to me."

Jessica's dad's name is Charlie Mintz and her mom's name is Sylvia Pepper.

How hard could it have been to name her Jessica Mintz-Pepper instead of Jessica Pepper-Mintz? If they'd had a name expert around, trust me, it never would have happened.

"You know, I take back what I said about this idea being dumb," Lucas said. "I think maybe you're on to something big here." ▉

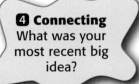

4 Connecting
What was your most recent big idea?

Vo·cab·u·lary

hyphenated (HY fuh nay tuhd) connected with a hyphen

"Yeah? You think?" I said.

"Yeah. And you know, once business takes off, you might even need a partner," Lucas said excitedly. "We could call it Experts, Incorporated."

"We?" I laughed. "I thought you were going to pitch for the Yankees."

Lucas smiled and shrugged.

"I doubt I'll get picked up; I can't even throw a <u>slider</u>. But if you want a partner who really understands why the world needs name experts, I'm your man, Rodd-o."

Mrs. Greenberg came down the aisle collecting the papers. As I handed her mine, I heaved a huge sigh of relief. Not only had I avoided ruining the pizza party, I'd managed to plan my entire future too, and it was looking pretty bright, if I do say so myself. ○

Answering the BIG Question

As you do the following activities, consider the Big Question:
What brings out the best in you?

WRITE TO LEARN What do you want to do when you grow up? Does the job you want to do exist already? If not, go ahead and invent it. Write an entry in your Learner's Notebook about your dream job.

PARTNER TALK Meet with another student who has read this story. Discuss whether you think children should be allowed to change their names if they don't like the ones their parents gave them.

Vo•cab•u•lary

slider (SLY dur) a kind of fast baseball pitch that curves as it approaches the plate

Why Music Matters:
Program Helps Students Learn to Tune In to Life

by Kari K. Ridge

Never underestimate the power of music to change lives.

A few years ago, Kevin Davis almost gave up on school. He hated math. He just didn't get it. Nothing else made much sense either.

Then Kevin found the power of music.

Kevin joined a program at his school called MusicAlive. The program uses music to help teach math and history. It also teaches things about English and geography.

For example, students learn that Detroit, Michigan, is known for its Motown sound. They also learn about the auto industry and sports teams in Detroit.

"MusicAlive changed my life," said Kevin, who is now 16. "It gave me confidence and a whole new outlook on school and on life." **1**

Kevin is now on the honor roll at his school in Chicago, Illinois. He loves to sing in the style of jazz legend Louis Armstrong. Kevin wants to study music in college.

> **1 Connecting**
> What does music do for you?

Getting Connected

Orbert Davis and Mark Ingram started MusicAlive five years ago. Both men have played in many bands. Davis is a trumpet player. He also writes music for TV shows and movies.

When Davis and Ingram were going to school, music kept them out of trouble.

They say they were too busy jamming with their bands. Now they want music to have the same impact on today's kids.

Davis and Ingram want to help students who are getting in trouble and having a hard time with school.

"So many kids are failing at reading," Davis says. "There is a link between reading and music. We are teaching life skills and showing that learning is fun."

Turning Around

In MusicAlive, Ashley Thornton learned to play drums. The 14-year-old girl also learned to play a recorder, which looks like a clarinet.

"We did fun road trips in our imagination where we learned about every kind of music," Ashley said. "I didn't even know it at the time, but I was also learning how to use real English instead of slang."

Fighting was just a way of life for Gregory Wallace, who is 11. He was suspended from school and failing math. He learned respect and discipline last year through MusicAlive. Gregory learned to get along with other students and to focus on his work.

Staying Focused

Teachers and principals say MusicAlive can help any kid change bad behavior.

Sidney Miller grew up poor in a Chicago housing project. Today, she is a teacher with MusicAlive. She plays the clarinet in jazz bands. She knows about the power of music.

When she was 11, Miller was invited to be in a gang. "But I was a member of the school band, so I was already a part of something," she says. "My music was much bigger than a gang could ever be."

She adds, "I stayed focused on music and kept out of trouble." ○

Answering the BIG Question

As you do the following activities, consider the Big Question:
What brings out the best in you?

WRITE TO LEARN Think about the different ways students have been affected by MusicAlive. What has music brought into their lives? Write down your thoughts in a brief entry in your Learner's Notebook.

PARTNER TALK Meet with a classmate who has read this article. Discuss how students at your school might react to a program like this. Would they want to be involved in it? Why or why not?

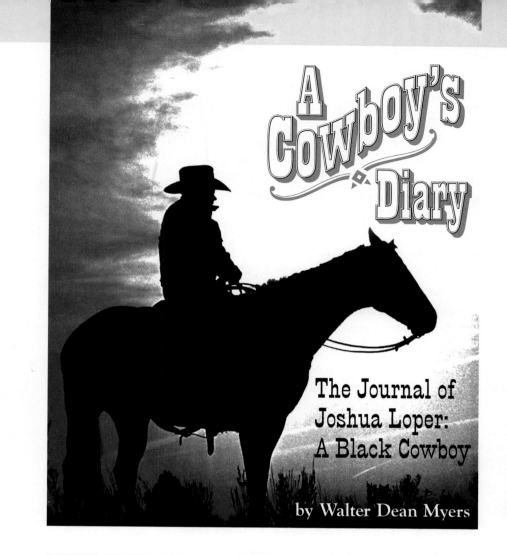

A Cowboy's Diary

The Journal of Joshua Loper: A Black Cowboy

by Walter Dean Myers

A young man goes on a real-life cattle drive and learns about the tough, gritty life of a cowboy in the 1800s.

In 1871, on the dusty plains of Texas, there lived a boy named Joshua Loper. The Civil War had ended in 1865, and slavery was now outlawed throughout the land. But black people like Joshua and his mother still faced terrible poverty and prejudice. Though Joshua was bright and hardworking, there were few opportunities for him.

A Cowboy's Diary

One day, a man called Captain Hunter came calling. The Captain was looking for boys—cowboys—to help on a cattle drive. ❶ In those days, cattle roamed freely through the wide-open spaces of the South and the West. Cowboys were needed to get the giant herds to the railroads, where they would be shipped to market in Chicago and New York. A small group of cowboys, riding on horseback, would "drive" thousands of cattle across hundreds of miles of open land.

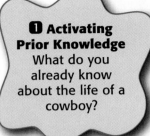

❶ **Activating Prior Knowledge**
What do you already know about the life of a cowboy?

The work was dusty, dirty, and dangerous. But 16-year-old Joshua Loper jumped at the chance to go. Working on the trail was a chance to earn decent money. More important, men on the trail were judged by their skills, not by the color of their skin.

That first cattle drive took Joshua from Texas up to Abilene, Kansas. The trip took nearly three months. On the following pages, you will read parts of Joshua's diary. It chronicles that incredible time in his life, from the days when America was still wild.

May 4, 1871

The captain said we were going to start out on Monday morning, soon as it made daylight. Mama was a little upset as I thought she would be. I hate to see her sad, but being on the trail and being a regular hand was pulling on me something fierce. I knew I would do right by Mama and hoped she would be proud of the way I went on with myself.

There were 10 other cowboys on the drive with Joshua. Among them were Captain Hunter, whom everyone called simply "the Captain," and Doom and Chubb, who worked alongside Joshua. There was also Isaiah, a former slave, who was the cook.

May 5

The Captain got the herd started at daybreak. Me and Doom were the drags, which meant we had to ride behind the herd. The Captain made it clear what we were supposed to do. "Don't let them stop. Don't let them get out of line. And don't get them moving too fast."

The Captain was tall and so thin his body looked like a bow ready to shoot off an arrow in your direction. His eyes were a light blue, and he had a way of fixing them on you that made you wish you could be someplace else.

The afternoon was easy, but it was a long day. I was tired and my back was aching. We watered the herd and bedded them down for the night. For supper we had stew, beans, coffee, and corn pone. It was delicious.

One night, rustlers rode through the herd and made off with 40 head of cattle. Joshua and the others tried to stop them. But they got away. The Captain knew that Joshua was a good shooter, so he took him along with one other man to hunt down the thieves.

June 11

We rode for hours without saying anything. A little past noon, the Captain stopped us. I was dog tired and the horses were beat. "They got to be over that ridge," the Captain said. The Captain took his rifle from its <u>scabbard</u> and I did the same. Me and the Captain crept toward the ridge. On top, he took off his hat and looked over. I did the same. There were cattle there, about 40 head. There were also four men.

"Shoot the one with the leather chaps," the Captain said.

"Kill him?" I asked. The Captain did not say nothing, just looked at me with a look hard enough to light a match on. I aimed real careful, close as I could without shooting him. Maybe they would run off if they knew they were being shot at. I held my breath and pulled the trigger just as my daddy had taught me. Soon as I got that shot off, I saw the cowboy with the leather chaps fall straight back. He was grabbing for his head and the others grabbing for their guns. I fired off another shot, and another one of them fell.

The Captain ran over to them and took their guns. Then he looked them over.

I glanced down at the men I had shot and saw they were still alive, much to my relief.

Vo•cab•u•lary

scabbard (SKA burd) a pouch or container for a gun or knife

"Now you mangy dogs got one minute to get out of gun range," he said. "So you better run fast."

They all started running.

Then we mounted up and got the cattle and started back to the camp.

Everybody was slapping me on the back and saying they knew I was a real man. I thanked the good Lord that I had not killed nobody.

I could see that the Captain still did not like me all that much, but when he needed somebody to do something he got me to do it.

Cowboys faced many dangers on the trail, including illness, injury, and hostile Indians. There was always the risk of a stampede, when the herd began running out of control without warning. This often led to disaster.

June 21

This was our worst stampede yet. They were moving fast, their hooves drumming along the flat ground, and we went after them. The dust was coming up so fast I started choking and pulled my kerchief up over my nose with one hand. I came real close to falling.

Finally we got them near to stopped. We moved in on them and herded them together in a jumble until they had stopped good.

"Where's the new guy?" Doom asked. **2**

I got a sick feeling in my stomach, but I did not say nothing. We moved away from the herd and watched it. We saw a little commotion on one side and some beeves moving away from a spot and bellowing. Wade went into the herd and it was him that found the new guy.

2 Predicting
What do you think happened to the new guy?

There was not much of him left. It was all white meat and bone, and you could not even tell where his left arm had been. The only way you knew it was a cowpuncher was the boots.

Vo·cab·u·lary

beeves (beevz) cattle; plural of *beef*
cowpuncher (KOW punch ur) cowboy

We got his _slicker_ and gathered him up in it. The cattle had just stomped him to death and had ground all his insides into the ground. The horse he was riding was dead, too.

Chubb, me, and Isaiah dug a grave, and we laid the cowboy in it. We took our hats off and the Captain prayed over him and I thought he meant every bit of it. It made me think that maybe I did not know the Captain as much as I thought I did.

When we bedded down nobody talked about what had happened, but it was with everybody. Stampedes could happen any minute and you could lose your life as easy as the cowboy did that afternoon, and we all knew that.

June 22

I have finally figured out what this trailing is all about. It is about riding a horse slowly alongside these cattle for mile after mile and making sure they don't have to work too hard. Then it's about making sure they have enough grass to graze even though you are too tired to scratch where you itch. It's about making sure the beeves don't get too thirsty even if all you have to drink is water so foul you got to strain it through the sweat of your neckerchief. Last, it's about calming them down every night and singing to them so they don't feel lonely, even though you have not seen the ones you love for weeks.

For a cowboy, a favorite horse is a dear and _cherished_ friend. Joshua had brought his own horse, Pretty, on the drive with him. The trail is hard on horses. And during the trip Pretty became weak and sick. Finally, it was clear that Pretty was dying.

July 3

"Your horse is waiting for you, boy."

That was what the Captain said when I come in to have breakfast.

I went over to where Pretty was half sitting down. When he saw

---

Vo·cab·u·lary

slicker (SLIK ur) raincoat
cherished (CHAIR isht) beloved

me he got to his feet and I could see it was a real struggle. Chubb came up behind me and handed me his rifle.

O Lord, it was the worst thing I ever had to do in my life. I put a bridle on Pretty and walked with him. The land was flat and you could see for just miles around. We walked, Pretty and me, real slow to where there were some trees. I told Pretty that I really loved him, that there was no other horse in the world that I would ever love as much as him. I think he knew I was telling the truth.

I took him behind the trees and he laid down and I sat down with him and held his head and ran my fingers through his mane. I did not want him to look at me because if he had seen how I looked with the tears down my face he might have thought he had done something wrong, which he had not.

I told him I was sorry and then I stood up with the rifle. Pretty tried to stand up, but I patted his neck and he laid down again. He was really suffering bad, and I had known it for a while. I said a prayer for him and then I used the rifle.

I will not be in this business for long. I think I will get some more book learning and maybe teach school or look for a job on a farm.

I do not want to be around no more cattle and no more horses. ❸

After two more weeks of hard riding, the crew finally made it to Abilene.

❸ **Predicting**
Do you think Joshua was serious about finding a different job?

July 14

It took half the day for us to load the herd into a freight train, and it might have been the longest half day I have spent. A lot of other cowboys helped us and some people working for the train company, which was the Kansas Pacific.

When we finished loading the herd we were done. We all started whooping and yelling.

I felt proud that I had come all the way from Texas without messing up. I had got the job done. Like a man should.

Epilogue

Between 1871 and 1882, Joshua Loper made eight more drives. In 1883, he was the trail boss on a drive from Texas to Ellsworth, Kansas. That's when he decided finally to put an end to his days as a cowboy. He eventually got married and settled in Texas, where he worked as an agent for a meat packer. His wife, Carrie, started a school for black children. They had one son. Joshua's journal was found in a big envelope with an old Civil War pouch and a tattered neckerchief. The envelope was labeled "Cowboy Stuff." ○

Answering the BIG Question

As you do the following activities, consider the Big Question:
What brings out the best in you?

WRITE TO LEARN Think about the different things Joshua learned on the cattle drive. Write a brief entry in your Learner's Notebook describing some of them.

LITERATURE GROUPS Meet with two or three others who have read this diary. Discuss why Joshua was willing to leave his home and his family for a tough, dangerous job.

I Jump Field

by Christa Champion

What does it feel like to throw your body into the air—to defy gravity?

Some people like sprinting
there's no time for thinking
all out, point to point, in a dash;

the pistol-shot start
the lurch of your heart
one burst, and you're done in a flash.

some prefer distance
the pure <u>perseverance</u>
when you cannot go on, but you do;

Vo•cab•u•lary

perseverance (pur suh VEER uns) the action of continuing to do something, even though it's hard

lap after lap
try to break from the pack
but in the end, it's the stopwatch and you.

what I like is jumping
the launching and leaping
the way that my whole body sails;

suspended in air
i am loosed from my cares
for a moment, gravity fails. ❶

there are those who like throwing
the spinning and heaving
then watching the arc of the toss;

while the hurdler's decision
is to strive for precision
to clear hurdles without a step lost.

but still i like jumping
both the long and the high
the secrets of flying revealed;

"do you run track?"
i am often asked
"no," i reply, "i jump field!"

❶ **Connecting**
What makes
you forget your
worries for
a while?

Vo•cab•u•lary

suspended (sus PEND ud) hanging
precision (pri SIH zhun) the condition of being exact

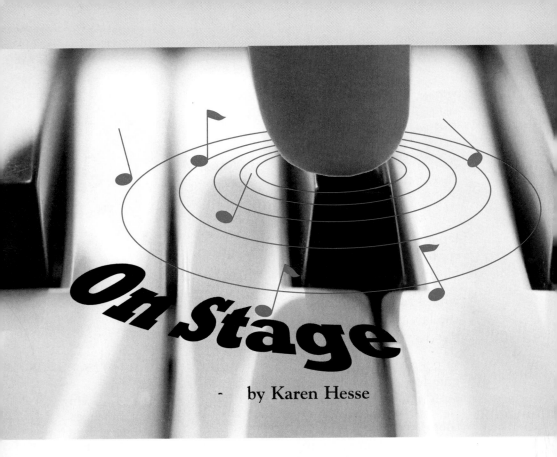

On Stage

by Karen Hesse

How can playing music be almost magical?

When I point my fingers at the keys,
   the music
springs straight out of me.
   Right hand
playing notes sharp as
   tongues,
telling stories while the
   smooth
buttery rhythms back me up
   on the left.

Folks sway in the
   Palace aisles
grinning and stomping and

out of breath,
and the rest, eyes shining,
    fingers snapping,
feet tapping. It's the best
    I've ever felt,
playing hot piano,
    sizzling with
Mad Dog,
    swinging with the Black Mesa Boys,
or on my own,
    crazy,
pestering the keys.
    That is
heaven. ❶
    How supremely
heaven
    playing piano
can be. ○

January 1934

❶ **Connecting**
What activity feels like heaven to you?

Answering the BIG Question

As you do the following activities, consider the Big Question:
What brings out the best in you?

WRITE TO LEARN Think about how different things bring out the best in the two speakers. When are you at your best, and how does it feel? Write a short poem in your Learner's Notebook about how it feels to be at your best.

LITERATURE GROUPS Meet with two or three classmates who have read these poems. Talk about the activities that bring out the best in you. Discuss ways to share how you feel while doing these activities.

Vo•cab•u•lary
pestering (PES tur ing) bothering

BREAKING DOWN THE WALLS:
I felt as if a wall divided me from the popular group.

by Kathryn D. Sullivan

What's really stopping you from getting to know other people?

By the time I was nine, I was a well-established tomboy. I liked sports, exploring, fishing, flying airplanes with my dad, and making up adventures with kids from my neighborhood in southern California.

One morning before school, there was a knock on my front door. When I answered, I was shocked to see a girl named Marsha. I knew her from school. She was part of a group of popular girls. Her group wasn't like mine. They didn't look like me or act like me. I felt as if a wall divided me from them.

Marsha thought a car had been trailing her, and she asked if she could come inside. I couldn't believe that she even knew where I lived, but somehow she did. And when she needed help, she knocked on my door.

Marsha's moment of need broke down the wall I'd imagined between us. She wasn't so different from me after all. From then on, we were friends. It was a moment of discovery, the first time I realized that the pictures we think people have of us are often wrong. ❶

❶ Activating Prior Knowledge
Do you think this is true, based on your own experience?

This lesson came back to me when I interviewed with NASA. I walked into a roomful of military officers, test pilots, and scientists. Oh, man! I thought. These guys won't think I belong here.

I could have stewed over the picture in my head, but I remembered the lesson Marsha taught me. I'm going to do what I can do, be who I am, have a good time, and see where it all comes out, I decided.

By the end of the week, I realized that it didn't matter what the others thought because I could do the job. And I did. I became an astronaut.

Dr. Kathryn D. Sullivan was part of the first space-shuttle astronaut class and flew three missions. During her first spaceflight, in October 1984, she became the first American woman to walk in space. She now leads one of the country's <u>premier</u> science museums, the Center of Science and Industry (COSI) in Columbus, Ohio. ○

Dr. Kathryn D. Sullivan

Answering the BIG Question

As you do the following activities, consider the Big Question:
What brings out the best in you?

WRITE TO LEARN Do you have friends among different social groups? Do you think it's difficult for such friendships to exist? Why or why not? Jot down your ideas in your Learner's Notebook. As you write, think about Kathryn's experience with Marsha.

LITERATURE GROUPS Meet with another student who has read this article. Discuss how Kathryn used her experience with Marsha to help her overcome her fears of fitting in at NASA. Have you had a similar experience that helped bring out the best in you?

Vo•cab•u•lary

premier (prih MEER) most important

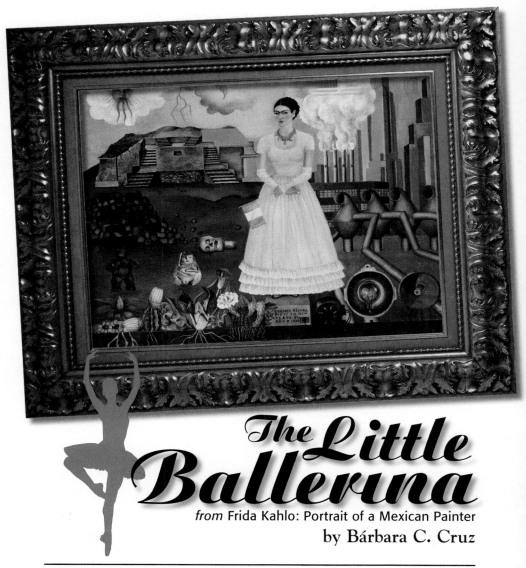

The Little Ballerina

from Frida Kahlo: Portrait of a Mexican Painter

by Bárbara C. Cruz

In the aftermath of a terrible accident, a painter is born.

Frida and Alejandro felt lucky that they were able to catch the new, brightly painted, wooden bus back home. They had just gotten on board when they realized Frida had lost the little toy umbrella Alejandro had bought for her. They left the bus and retraced their steps, but were not able to find the umbrella. Now, with a colorful cup-and-ball toy in hand, they found seats together in the back of the bus and hoped they would be home soon.

The bus driver must have been in a hurry, too. He tried to quickly steer the bus to pass in front of a turning streetcar, but he misjudged the timing. The heavy streetcar could not stop and crashed into the bus, splitting it apart and throwing the passengers onto the street.

Alejandro awakened to find himself underneath the streetcar and the front of his coat gone. But where was Frida? After searching among the bodies for a few moments, Alejandro found Frida covered in blood with a steel handrail piercing her stomach. Another passenger's packet of gold powder had opened during the accident and spilled on Frida. People were yelling to help *la bailarina* (the little ballerina). With the gold sprinkled on her body, everyone thought she was a dancer.

A man shouted, "We have to take out the rod!" He put his knee on Frida's body and pulled the handrail. Frida screamed with pain. She was carried to a nearby table until the Red Cross arrived. Her spine, pelvis, collarbone, ribs, and right leg and foot were broken in the accident. Her condition was so serious that when the medics arrived, they did not think she could be saved and hurried to help others who had a better chance of surviving. Only five other passengers survived the crash.

After she was taken to the hospital, several surgeries were done to set the broken bones. Doctors were not sure she would live, telling her: "By rights you should be dead." After they knew she would survive, doctors still did not know whether Frida would ever be able to walk again. Frida was only eighteen years old. ❶

❶ **Predicting**
How will the accident change Frida's life?

Vo•cab•u•lar•y

streetcar (STREET kar) a form of public transportation that runs on rails set into city streets

When her family found out about the accident, they were horrified. They were so scared of seeing Frida in her condition, they did not visit her. Only her sister Matilde went to the hospital to sit with Frida. Her mother was so shocked by the accident that she did not speak for a month.

For a long time Frida had to lay flat on her back in a plaster cast. She was not even able to sit up. She wrote to her friend:

Last Friday a cast was put on and since then it has been real torture. . . There is a dreadful pain in my lungs and all over my back. I cannot touch my leg, I cannot walk, and I sleep badly. Imagine, for two and a half hours, they had me hanging by my head only and after that resting on the tips of my toes for over one hour, while the cast was dried with heated air. . . For three or four months I must bear this torture, and if I don't get relief I would sincerely like to die.

Although her healing was slow, doctors were still amazed at her progress. It seemed incredible, but within a few months she started walking again.

The Little Ballerina

The summer after the accident, though, Frida had a <u>relapse</u>. Once again, she had to lay in bed, flat on her back in a brace. ❷ As she started to get well, Frida became very bored at having to lay in bed day after day. Her father was an artist and she had watched him paint before, and even though she had never taken art lessons, Frida began to think about painting. Frida's mother had a special easel made for her so she could paint in bed, and her father lent her his box of oil paints and some brushes.

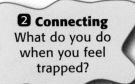

❷ Connecting
What do you do when you feel trapped?

Because she could not leave her room, her first paintings were of her family and the people who came to visit her. Using a mirror attached overhead to her bed's canopy, she painted her first self-portrait. This painting provided a hint of what was to come.

In many ways the streetcar accident changed Frida's life. She matured. She found physical and emotional strength she did not know she had. But most importantly, she discovered a love for painting that would change her life forever. ○

Answering the BIG Question

As you do the following activities, consider the Big Question:
What brings out the best in you?

WRITE TO LEARN Write an entry in your Learner's Notebook about a time when trouble or suffering brought out the best in a person. You can write about yourself or someone you know, or you can write about a person from history or current events.

PARTNER TALK Meet with another student who has read this selection. Discuss what you think it takes to be a great artist or writer. What kinds of life experiences may help an artist achieve greatness? Does suffering always lead to personal growth, as it did with Frida?

Vo·cab·u·lary

relapse (REE laps) condition in which an old illness or injury flares up again

ROCK
TAKES A NAME

by Tim Myers

Sometimes a journey can lead you right back to where you started.

Once in a village among the dark northern forests there lived a boy who had no real name yet—but he wanted one. As he worked around his family's lodge or hunted with his father or watched in the fields to keep crows from stealing the corn crop, he could feel himself growing stronger and wiser, and he could imagine himself as a man. But still he had no name to go with who he was becoming.

"A name is not something you just pick up off the ground," his mother and father said. "Sometimes other people give you your name, an elder or a <u>shaman</u>. Or it comes to you in what you do, or in a dream. You must be worthy of it—and you must be patient with its coming. When the time is right, you'll know."

Vo·cab·u·lary

shaman (SHAY mun) a holy person who uses magic to help people

Rock Takes a Name

Since the boy had no real name, and since he often played with little rocks, the people just called him Rock.

But one day Rock couldn't wait any longer. So he stood before his family as they sat by the lodge fire, his mother sewing deerskin leggings, his sister stringing beads, his father trimming arrow shafts. "I haven't found a name in my dreams, or in what I've done. So I'm going to look for one," he said. And since he had already seen ten winters, they let him go. ❶

❶ **Predicting**
Do you think Rock will find a name during his journey?

"I won't come back till I find a real name," Rock said.

He started walking through the sun-streaked forest to the west, away from the village, carrying his bow over his shoulder and a few of the arrows he'd made in his leather quiver. Soon he came to a rushing stream and began to cross it, downstream from a big abandoned beaver dam made even taller by tangled branches and sapling trunks from floods. Treading carefully on the slippery stones under the icy water, he thought "Maybe I'll take the name River-Crosser!"

But suddenly a big rotten trunk in the old dam gave way and the whole thing collapsed. Rock turned to see a wall of water as big as he was rushing straight for him.

"Hold on!" he told himself. "And don't let go!" He quickly pushed his feet down between the underwater stones and threw his arms around a tree trunk angling out from the bank. When the wall of freezing water and bunched branches hit him, he was almost carried away—but he held on till it passed.

With his heart still pounding and icy water running off his shoulders, he scrambled out of the stream. His feet ached. Among the branches above him, a cardinal was singing as if nothing had happened. "I could have drowned!" he told himself. "I don't want to be River-Crosser."

Vo·cab·u·lary

shafts (shafts) the long handles of spears or other weapons

He kept walking. After a time he came to a valley his father had never taken him into. He recognized it from a boulder slide surrounded by low sumac trees. "This is not our land," his father would say, pointing with his bow. "Only a war party would go that way, to fight our enemies."

"Perhaps my name is hidden in there," Rock told himself. "I could be Far-Walker!" He went in.

But as he crept among the dense trees and undergrowth, he heard a twig snap somewhere in front of him. "Be quiet!" he told himself. "Don't make a sound!" So he froze where he was, settling to his knees behind a maple trunk and some chokecherry bushes, hardly daring to breathe.

In a moment or two a big man with a bow and arrow emerged from the bushes, not twenty steps away. His hair and clothes were different— an enemy! The man looked around carefully, standing still a long time, almost like a wolf sniffing the air. Then he slowly continued on his way, back up into the valley.

Rock knew the man was hunting, since he wasn't painted for war and carried only a hunter's weapons. If he hadn't snapped the twig, Rock would have walked right into him!

Now he was afraid to move. What if the enemy hunter knew he was there and was trying to lure him out of hiding? Or what if prey led him back to this spot? Rock's muscles began to ache. Sweat trickled down his face, and the mosquitoes soon found him. But for a long time he didn't move or make any sound. Then he slipped away and hurried back through the woods, past the boulder slide and out of the valley.

"Far-Walker doesn't feel right either," he thought. **❷**

❷ Questioning
Do you understand why Far-Walker doesn't work as a name for Rock?

Still he pressed on, circling to the south and then east, determined to find a name even as he shivered with the danger he'd just escaped. As the sun began sinking he came to a low cliff above a lake, its blue water brilliant in the <u>waning</u> light. The air was getting cooler as twilight came on, and he could see the evening star in the west above the treetops. Just then three loons rose past him and flew off into the salmon-colored sky. "I wish I could go with them," he thought. "Maybe I'll take the name Loon!" So he pretended to fly by flapping his arms.

Suddenly he heard laughter. There were more loons down on the lake, and their high-pitched cries sounded as if they were making fun of him.

At first this made him angry and embarrassed. Then he thought about it. "They're laughing because I'm trying to be one of them—but I'm not a loon! I can only pretend." Then he remembered how good it felt to sit by the fire with his mother and father and sister in their lodge on a cold night. That made him homesick. Besides, he was hungry, and the thought of moose stew with roasted corn made his mouth water. He set off for the village.

He knew they would ask if he'd found a name. So as he walked beneath the darkening trees, he thought about everything he'd done. "When the beaver dam broke and the water came rushing, I didn't move—I held my ground. When the

---

Vo•cab•u•lary

waning (WAYN ing) getting smaller or going away

enemy hunter passed, I was perfectly silent. And when the loons laughed at me, I realized I should be who I am, and that I have my own place in this world."

Coming out of the woods toward the village, he could smell the cooking fires and see thin lines of blue smoke rising from the smoke holes of the lodges. "But what about a name?" he thought. So he asked himself, "What is it that holds firm without moving, is always silent and still, and is happy in its own place?"

Suddenly he knew.

They were waiting for him when he entered the lodge. "Well, my son," his mother asked, "did you find a name?"

"Yes," he said proudly. "From now on I will be called . . . Rock!" ○

Answering the
BIG Question

As you do the following activities, consider the Big Question:
What brings out the best in you?

WRITE TO LEARN Think about what Rock hoped to discover on his journey. Write a brief entry in your Learner's Notebook about what he actually found.

LITERATURE GROUPS Meet with two or three others who have read this folktale. Talk about what names you would give yourselves and why.

What's fair and what's not?

Is it possible to make life fairer? As you read the following selections, you'll discover a variety of ways in which to think about the question: **What's fair and what's not?** Some of the situations and characters may help you come up with your own answers to that question.

Key Reading Skills

As you read the selections in this unit, apply these reading skills.

- **Inferring** Use your own reason and experiences to guess what the author means but does not say outright.
- **Clarifying** Pause from time to time to make sure you understand what you have read, especially after difficult sections of text.
- **Distinguishing Fact from Opinion** Facts can be shown to be true. Opinions tell an author's or a character's feeling or belief about something.
- **Identifying Problem and Solution** Many selections present a problem and a solution, or a series of problems and solutions. Identifying these problems and solutions will help you understand what you read.

The Elian Gonzalez Story

by Michael Dahlie

A boy loses his mother during their flight to freedom—will he also lose his father, or will he lose his chance for freedom?

It all started in November 1999. It was Thanksgiving Day. Two men were fishing off the coast of Florida. Suddenly, the men spotted something strange in the distance. They could make out an inner tube, but something seemed to be strapped to it. They weren't sure what it was. After they got closer, they decided it was nothing. They thought it was just a rag doll. But then they saw its hand move and realized it was a little boy.

Quickly, they dived in to save him. When they pulled the boy onto the boat, he was shivering and asking for water. He had not had anything to drink for days. The fishermen rushed the boy to the hospital. He was badly sunburned and barely alive. But it looked like he was going to make it. The doctors called it a miracle. The fishermen who saved him were overjoyed. It was a short celebration, however. Soon they began to piece together the story of how the boy had ended up on the inner tube.

The boy's name was Elian Gonzalez. Four days earlier, he and his mother had set out for Florida from a beach in Cuba. Elian's mother and father were divorced, and his mother wanted to start a new life in the United States. She knew the boy and his father would miss each other. But she thought Elian would be better off in the U.S. Under Castro—Cuba's leader—people have few freedoms. And most Cubans are very poor. ❶

❶ **Clarifying**
Why did Elian's mother decide to leave Cuba?

Eleven other people were crowded in the boat with Elian and his mom. They all knew the journey would be dangerous. It was 90 miles across rough, shark-<u>infested</u> waters. And the boat they were traveling on was homemade and <u>flimsy</u>. But they were willing to risk it. They were determined to leave Cuba.

Vo•cab•u•lary

infested (in FES tud) filled with
flimsy (FLIM zee) thin or weak

The homemade museum Elian's uncle set up in his honor

On the second night of their journey, a storm blew in. The small boat couldn't handle the huge waves and heavy winds. Before long, the boat turned over. It sank. And it took six passengers with it.

There were only two inner tubes to hold the rest of the passengers. A man and a woman took one; Elian, his mother, and three other people grabbed hold of the other. Elian was strapped to the top of the inner tube. The rest of the <u>refugees</u> held on to the sides. But it soon became too hard to hold on. One-by-one the ocean took their lives. Poor Elian watched as his own mother slipped beneath the ocean's surface and drowned. The next people he would see would be the fishermen who saved him.

The news of Elian's story sent <u>shock waves</u> through Florida's large Cuban community. Elian's American relatives were told of the tragedy. Soon his great-uncle went to the hospital. He took Elian

Vo•cab•u•lary

refugees (ref yoo JEEZ) people who are forced to leave their home because of war, poverty, or other causes
shock waves (shok wayvs) major disruptions or reactions

back to his house in Little Havana. The boy was safe but scared. He wondered what was going to happen to him. Would he stay in the U.S.? Or would he return to Cuba to be with his father again? ❷

❷ Identifying Problem and Solution
What are two possible solutions to Elian's problem?

In most cases, it would be a simple decision. Most people would say that a boy who loses his mother should live with his father. But since Castro's communist government took control of Cuba forty years ago, Cuba and the U.S. have been enemies. The U.S. says that Castro's government mistreats its people and that Cubans are not free. And Elian's American family agrees. The family [members] said Cuba is a terrible place for a boy to grow up. They said it would be wrong to send Elian back to Cuba. He would have no money and none of the freedoms people in the U.S. have.

But Elian's father thought differently. When he heard that his son was alive, he demanded that Elian be returned to Cuba. Elian's father said that it was wrong for a boy to grow up without his parents. He said Elian belonged with him—his father. Cuban President Fidel Castro and his government quickly took the father's side. A major showdown was beginning to brew.

Soon, people in both Cuba and the United States were talking about Elian. What might have been just an argument between family members became an argument between nations. Huge protests were held in Cuba. People were demanding Elian's return. Castro even sent Elian's grandfather and father to Washington, D.C., to bring Elian back in person.

Protests were also held in Little Havana. People began to surround the house of Elian's uncle. They stayed near the house day and night. Everyone was saying that Elian should remain in the U.S. They held posters with Elian's picture. They chanted and sang and prayed. And they spent the nights in tents set up on the streets. Police officers and reporters were everywhere. Politicians showed up. Even celebrities like singer Gloria Estefan joined in. The protesters were determined to keep Elian in the U.S.

The Elian Gonzalez Story

The protests in Cuba and Miami lasted for months. No one was willing to give in. But the fact was that neither group had the power to decide Elian's future. In the end, it was up to the United States Government and Attorney General Janet Reno to make the decision.

Working with several lawyers, Janet Reno carefully looked at the facts of the case. She weighed both sides of the problem and considered Elian's needs. Eventually she made a choice. She decided that the boy should go back to Cuba. She agreed that it would be good for Elian to grow up in the United States. But she thought it was more important for Elian and his father to be together.

Elian's father was thrilled. He was in Washington, D.C. and anxious to see his son. But Elian's American relatives were furious. They understood why the boy should be with his father. But they didn't want Elian to go back to Cuba. Elian was living with them, and they wanted it to stay that way. They told Janet Reno that they didn't want to nor would they give the boy up.

Janet Reno stood firm. She listened to the family's concerns, but she said that the boy must be returned. She said that it was wrong for Elian and his father to be apart any longer. Still, the family delayed handing the boy over.

So Reno took action. In the early morning hours of April 22, 2000, she sent armed U.S. officials to the home of Elian's American relatives. They burst into the house and took Elian by force. The protesters outside were angry. The relatives did not want to let Elian go. But none of them had any choice. Soon Elian was on a plane. Within hours, he was with his father in Washington, D.C. They had been separated for five months.

In the days that followed, many people were upset with Reno's actions. ❸ Newspapers printed pictures of armed men taking a crying Elian from his relatives. People wondered if Reno had used too

❸ **Distinguishing Fact from Opinion** Does this sentence state a fact or an opinion? How can you tell?

much force. But Reno defended her decision. She said it was a show of force, not the use of force. She pointed out that because of this show of force, no one was hurt. She also repeated that it was important that the boy be returned to his father immediately. It could not have waited any longer. Action was necessary.

But there were more pictures than the ones of the armed U.S. officials taking Elian. Newspapers also printed photographs of the reunion between Elian and his father. From the pictures, no one could doubt how happy the two were together. And all the eyewitness reports said the same thing. Elian and his father were overjoyed to see one another. Elian's father was laughing and crying, and so was Elian.

Today people are still debating Elian's case. The six-year-old boy nearly died, and he watched his own mother drown. He's been through a lot. It will be hard for him to get over his pain. People want to make sure he gets the help he needs.

Some people say Janet Reno's decision to send Elian back to Cuba with his father was a bad one. They say it will hurt him. Other people say the decision will help. But in the end, it's too early to say. Only time will tell. For now, most people agree that the best thing for Elian is to live as much of a normal life as possible. Hopefully, being with his father is at least a step in that direction. ○

Answering the BIG Question

As you do the following activities, consider the Big Question: **What's fair and what's not?**

WRITE TO LEARN Think about the decision Janet Reno had to make: send Elian back to Cuba or let him stay in the United States. Then write a brief entry in your Learner's Notebook explaining why you agree or disagree with her decision.

LITERATURE GROUPS Meet with two or three others who have read "The Elian Gonzalez Story." Discuss why the solution to Elian's problem became so complicated. Was it fair that he got caught in the middle of an argument between two countries?

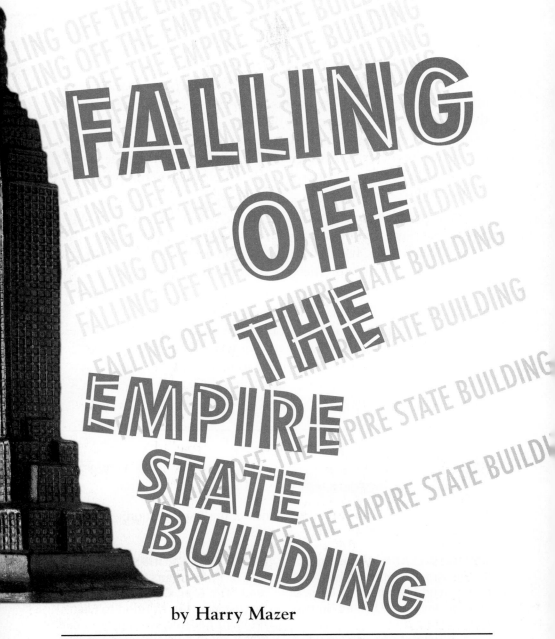

FALLING OFF THE EMPIRE STATE BUILDING

by Harry Mazer

A boy discovers that there may be more to life than playing games.

Vicik never came to my house and I never went to his house, but he was my friend, and it was like God was my friend. He was strong as a truck. He could run faster and hit a ball farther than anybody. He'd dare anything. Nothing could ever touch him.

What I remember best about him is <u>stickball</u>, the way he held the bat, waving it in a little circle over his head, just daring you to get the ball past him. He could hit a ball three sewers, from one end of Britain Street to the other. **1**

Britain Street was the best place to play stickball because there was hardly any traffic. All you needed was a taped-up broomstick and a rubber

1 Distinguishing Fact from Opinion
In these two paragraphs, what is fact and what is opinion about Vicik?

Vo·cab·u·lary

stickball (STIK bawl) game similar to baseball, played in the streets

ball. Every game had a season. There was a squirt gun season, a yo-yo season, and a season when we played street hockey on roller skates that we clamped to our shoes and tightened with special keys we kept on cords around our necks. We played stickball all year round.

Vicik and Dov were the leaders. Vicik tossed the bat to Dov, who tossed it back. They went fist over fist up the stick. Last hold got the first pick.

Dov was tall and skinny. He talked fast and stuttered, <u>spattering</u> spit in all directions. He always picked his pal, Jack, first. Vicik picked Leo. I would have picked him, too.

The strongest were chosen first, the fastest, the best hitters. The scare in my belly was big. "Choose me," I prayed. I didn't care if I was the last, as long as I played. It was shameful not to be picked. Vicik finally saw me and gave me the nod. "Okay, Lenny, you play out."

I ran out almost to the end of the street. I counted two manhole covers. "Hit the ball," I yelled. I slapped my hands together. I was small, but everyone said I had a man's voice. "All the way," I yelled, "hit it all the way to me!"

Vicik smiled at everything I did. If I missed the ball, he winked at me. And when I caught it, he said, "Thataway, Lenny."

My father never smiled at anything I did. All he said was,

Vo•cab•u•lary

spattering (SPAT ur ing) spraying out droplets

"I don't want you to play in the street." Where he came from, you either went to school or you went to work. He called my games "foolishness." Everything I did was "foolishness." He wanted me to stay in the house, do my homework, study, and listen to the opera like him. He always wanted me to do something I didn't want to do.

He didn't get it. We had to play in the street or we didn't play. Growing up in New York City, there were just the streets, the cement sidewalks, the stoops, the brick walls. No Little League, no grown-ups supervising games. Hardly any playgrounds.

We got chased by everyone: storekeepers afraid for their windows, and people who couldn't stand us playing stoopball against their steps. "Chickey!" Chickey was the call when a cop was coming. We ran, the cop after us. He got the bat, broke it in a sewer grate, and dropped the pieces down the hole. It was bad. A <u>heavy-duty</u> stick with a good taped handle was hard to find. ❷

It was all part of the game. The only place that belonged to us was the middle of the street. Us and the cars. "Heads up. Car coming!" Play stopped. We jeered at the drivers, dared them to brush against us. "Go on, move, get outta here!" we yelled.

❷ Clarifying
Why was playing in the streets hard sometimes?

Vo•cab•u•lary

heavy-duty (HEV ee DOO tee) strong and solidly built

Falling Off the Empire State Building

You had to have nerve. And never show fear. Once, on my bike, I grabbed the back of a moving truck. I was on one side and Vicik was on the other side. The truck went so fast my heart was down between my legs. I had to let go. But Vicik never let go.

We hopped rides on the <u>trolley</u> cars that ran up and down White Plains Road. If the <u>motorman</u> didn't see us, we could ride all the way to Burke Avenue or even Gun Hill Road. Every time the trolley stopped, we jumped off. When it started, we jumped on again. Hook a hand through the window, but keep ducked down. If the motorman spotted you, he'd whack your hand off. A kid in my class got bounced off the hood of a car that way and broke both his arms.

We flew kites on the roof and chased each other over the top. Being on the roof was like being on top of the world. We looked out over the rooftops. At night you could see the stars.

"Chicken! Let's see you walk the edge." Vicik walked the edge like it was nothing. On a dare, he hung over the edge, seven stories in the air, and let go. **3** The fire escape was right under him, but it scared me just to think about it. Once

> **3 Inferring**
> What did it take to be part of the narrator's group of friends?

Vo·cab·u·lary

trolley (TRAWL ee) old-fashioned form of public transportation, similar to a bus but running on rails set into the street
motorman (MOH tur man) trolley driver

I'd seen a dead man on the sidewalk, covered with a canvas. He'd been working on the building and slipped off a <u>scaffold</u>. His paint-stained boots stuck out from under the canvas.

My father didn't like me to go out. "Where are you going? Put something on." Like I was going out naked. I wasn't cold; he was. He never went out without getting all dressed up—suit, tie, hat, his shoes shined. He was like a soldier in uniform.

The first thing my father did in the morning was comb his hair. He combed it straight back, smooth and flat behind his ears. Then he exercised. He opened the window. My mother told him not to stand by the window in his underwear, in front of all the neighbors. "What neighbors? he said. "Who's looking?"

He stretched, he took deep breaths, everything deliberate and slow. He bent his knees, straightened up, then touched his toes. Then he combed his hair again.

He rubbed his hand over the bristle on his cheeks, then took out the shaving cream and the razor. That was the part I liked best. When he was done, he'd hand me the razor, but

Vo•cab•u•lary

scaffold (SKAF old) structure constructed next to a building to allow cleaners or other workers to work outside the upper stories

without the blade. I foamed up and ran the razor up and
down and all around my face like a sled in
the snow.

One time I decided I was going
to teach my father how to play.
We were on the street together,
and I was bouncing my ball.
"Catch," I said. "What?" he said.
I showed him the ball. I put the ball
in his hand. "Now you give it to
me, Pop." He handed me the ball,
then wiped his hands on his white
handkerchief.

I bounced the ball on the
sidewalk, then threw it to him,
nice and easy. He caught it.
"That's the way, Pop, good."

My dream was that my
father would learn about games
and play catch with me. He could
pitch to me and I could practice my
batting, which was not too great. I threw the ball
again, and it got away from him. He was wearing a coat
and a hat, and he couldn't bend. The ball slipped like water
through his fingers and rolled out in the street. "Grab it!" I yelled.
But he didn't move. He stood there like a dope.

I dove for the ball. It was my pink Spaldeen, the best ball
in the world. I saw the car coming, I had plenty of time, but my
father went nuts. "Stop!" His voice was like an explosion. "Are
you crazy?"

"Pop, my ball . . ." The car rolled over it and split it in half.
"My Spaldeen . . ." I picked up the pieces. The insides were pink
like bubble gum and it smelled like new rubber.

"How many times do I have to tell you: Stay out of the street,"
my father said. "All you do is play. Play is not important. School
is important."

I didn't say anything. Underneath everything, I knew I didn't have to listen to him, because he wasn't a real American. When I thought that, it made me feel sorry for him. I was born here and he wasn't. I knew I was going to leave him behind. ❹

❹ Clarifying
Why does the narrator think he's better than his father?

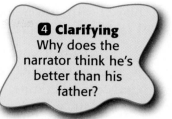

There was never a moment when I felt he understood. He was from another world. He had nothing to teach me. I learned from my friends, from Vicik. There was nothing I needed from my father, except maybe to teach me how to shave or make a tie.

On Saturday I was out of the house early. Out of the dark rooms, the corridors, the tension. "Stop! Stand still a minute." They were both on me. Mother and Father. One of them says, "Where are you going?" The other one says, "You didn't eat anything yet."

I hardly heard them. I was out, up the stairs and over the roof. It had rained overnight and there were puddles in all the dips.

The air was clear and clean and taut as a wire. I couldn't breathe enough of it. One last breath and I dove down another dark, spooky staircase. I pounded on a door. "Let's go, Mutt." He was my real friend.

He wanted me to come inside. I looked past him down the dark corridor of his apartment. His mother was in the kitchen, and he had to finish eating before she'd let him out.

I waited in front of the building. Mutt and I were

handball partners. I was left-handed and that was an advantage, because our strong arms were on the outside. I liked to watch the older guys play. They played the same game we did, only they played with gloves and a small hard black ball. Those were things I really wanted, a pair of leather gloves and a regulation handball.

I had a ball in my pocket. I bounced it, threw it up, caught it. Besides the ball, I carried marbles in my pockets, trading cards, a pocketknife, coins. We played marbles in the dirt. I used my biggest, smoothest marble as a shooter. The little ones were emmies, and there were steelies and clearies you held up to the light. We matched pennies, playing odds and evens, or pitched them against a wall. Or you could put a coin on the crack in the sidewalk, then try to hit it with a ball to the next crack.

Vo·cab·u·lary

handball (HAND bawl) sport played by using one's hands to hit a small ball against a wall
regulation (reg yoo LAY shun) made according to the official rules of the sport

Sometimes, if no boys were around I'd play potsie with the girls. You chalked the game on the sidewalk, eight numbered squares. You dropped a bottle cap or a stone into square one, hopped on one foot through all the squares, picked up the marker, and hopped out.

Mutt and I played handball all morning. When I got home my hands were swollen, my fingers fat like sausages. Nobody was home, but my mother had left me a sandwich, a glass of milk, and a big piece of yellow sponge cake. I ate and then fell down on the bed, sank down into pillows and quilts. I heard cars honking through the open windows, sirens, kids calling. The window curtains blew in and out.

When I woke up, I didn't know where I was. I staggered out to the other room. My mother was cutting a pattern for a dress on the table. My father was telling her she was going to ruin everything. I ate noodle pudding and washed it down with a glass of milk.

"I'm going out." I had the door open.

"Where are you going? Shut the door and come back inside."

"My friends are waiting."

"You've been out enough. Sit. Read something."

My father read the paper. I went to the refrigerator and got the white bread and butter.

"Are you eating again?" he said. "If you're eating, sit down. Only animals eat standing up." **5**

I sat down. My father turned a page,

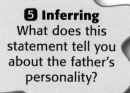

5 Inferring
What does this statement tell you about the father's personality?

wet a finger, and turned another page. I could hear the kids outside through the open windows. It was getting dark. I leaned on my elbow. In the distance, along the horizon, along the edge of the sky and the rooftops, I saw a train creeping along the elevated track.

The paper rustled, then slipped from my father's hand. I waited till his eyes closed. I had my sneakers off. I held them up for my mother to see as I tiptoed out of the room.

In the bedroom, I looked out the window. The sky was still bright above, but below in the courtyard it was dark. I hung out the window and saw Vicik's blond head shining. I bird-whistled. "Vicik, up here."

I dangled my sneakers out the window, let one go, and then the other. They fell five floors, straight down. Vicik caught them. He motioned for me to come down. I went out the fire escape window, down the narrow metal stairs. On the last landing, I was still too high. Vicik reached up. "Leggo." He had his arms out. "Leggo, Lenny."

I let go, fell into his arms, and we both went down. I laced on my sneakers, and we ran off to find the others.

There were a million moths around the streetlights. The best game at night was Johnny on the Pony. We divided into two big teams. I was on Vicik's team. Dov's team made itself into a horse first.

The fattest boy, the pillow boy, stood with his back to the wall. The other boys on his team bent over and locked together, head to

Vo·cab·u·lary

elevated (EL uh vay tud) lifted up; higher than street level tail, making the horse. The last boy tucked his head between the legs of the boy in front of him. "Anyone who farts gets killed."

Our team was across the street. I was the first one to run, because I was the smallest. "Go, Lenny!" Vicik yelled. I sprinted, picked up speed. I got my knees high, let my arms swing. "Go, Lenny!" I vaulted over the bent back of the last boy and threw myself as far forward on the horse as I could. I came down hard on somebody's bony back. The next boy landed on top of me, and the next, and the next, one on top of the other, digging in, hanging on.

I looked back. There came Vicik. His arms were pumping. His feet were shooting out like a duck's. His eyes were popping out of his head. He went up higher than anyone and came down on top of us like a ton of bricks. It was like an earthquake. The horse trembled. It started to shake and crack and fall apart.

"Johnny on the Pony," the other team chanted. They had to say it three times. "Johnny on the Pony . . . Johnny . . ." But they

couldn't. The horse swayed one way and then the other. And then it fell. We won.

After the game broke up, a bunch of us hung around the candy store. Vicik sat on a fire hydrant and poked at his teeth with a straw. He was telling us a joke and laughing in the middle of it. "What did the moron say when he jumped off the Empire State Building?" Vicik was laughing so hard he could hardly get out the punch line. "He's falling, and someone says, 'How's it going?' And the moron says, 'So far so good.'"

Gradually, everyone went home, but I was still there with Vicik. I knew I should go home, but it was Vicik, and I couldn't. He bought a candy bar and we shared it. We walked around Allerton Avenue, all the way up to Boston Post Road. It was late and there was almost nobody on the street. Vicik's house was off Mace Avenue. I'd never been on that street. The sidewalk was all broken up, and there were no apartment houses, just a lot of trees and old wooden houses.

The lights were on inside his house, but he didn't go in. "Is your father waiting up for you?" I knew my father was going to kill me. Vicik just shrugged.

We walked along the edge of the curb, talking a little. I kept waiting for him to say he was going in, so I could leave. He kept talking, telling jokes. He sat down on his steps, leaning forward with his head in his hands. He stopped talking. **6**

"What's the matter?" I said. He shook his head.

6 Clarifying
Why can't Lenny go home?

Finally, I couldn't stay another second. "I'm going," I said. I knew I was letting him down, but I couldn't help it. When I looked back, I saw him go into his house. I didn't know why, but I went back and stood on the sidewalk and looked in the window. I saw a man. He looked like Vicik, only bigger. I saw him push Vicik against the wall. Vicik fell back. He didn't raise his hand. He didn't defend himself. He stood with his back to the wall, his eyes on his father. When his father swung at him he ducked, and ducked again, but his father kept hitting him.

I ran all the way home. There was no traffic, nobody on the streets. When I got to my building, I took off my shoes and went up the stairs like a burglar. I turned my key in the lock and slipped inside. Then stood there, just inside the door, listening. I didn't hear anything but my own breathing.

Where were they? What if they were gone? It was the same thought I scared myself with sometimes when I woke up in the middle of the night. What if they said, Enough! They were sick of waiting for me, sick of my games, sick of trying to make me be good.

Then I heard something from the living room, where they sleep. Something moving, something big and dark, and creeping toward me. "Who's there?" It was white and big, and in the doorway. A ghost wearing white underwear.

"What are you doing?" my father said.

"Nothing."

"What are you standing by the door for?"

"I'm not." I laughed. It was dumb to laugh. I should have been sorry. Made an excuse. *There was an accident. . . . We had to go to the hospital . . . and the police station . . .*

"You're laughing? You come home at this time and you're laughing?"

From the other room, my mother called, "Don't get excited."

My father held the alarm clock. "You see what time it is?"

"I don't know."

"It's twelve on the clock. What were you doing till twelve o'clock?"

"Playing Johnny on the Pony."

"With horses, you play with horses at twelve o'clock?"

"*We're* the horses, Pop. It's only a game.

He sat down "You're a horse now? What kind of game is that?"

"It's teams, Pop. It's like tug-of-war. It's fun."

For a long time he sat there, rocking forward and back with the clock in his lap. "A game." He repeated it several times, rocking back and forth.

"Gonif," he said, finally. "American gonif." American thief. "In this country, you can get away with anything." **7** Then he told me to go to bed, and I did. ○

> **7 Distinguishing Fact from Opinion**
> Is the father stating a fact or an opinion?

Answering the BIG Question

As you do the following activities, consider the Big Question: **What's fair and what's not?**

WRITE TO LEARN In the story, Lenny doesn't seem to feel his parents treat him fairly. In your Learner's Notebook, write whether you think Lenny is being fair to his parents. Give your reasons.

LITERATURE GROUPS Join with two or three other students who have read this story. Discuss what Lenny's father says at the very end. Do you think all the characters in the story get away with something? Do you agree with his statement about Americans in general?

Elizabeth Eckford:
Facing a Mob on the First Day of School

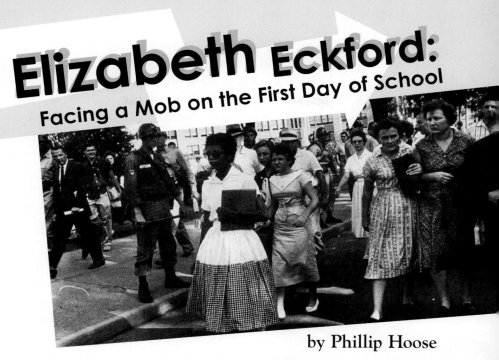

by Phillip Hoose

Nine students refused to believe that their actions wouldn't matter—and they made a big difference in the struggle to end racial segregation in schools.

Little Rock, Arkansas, September 4, 1957

Elizabeth Eckford was a fifteen-year-old tenth grader in the fall of 1957. She was one of the Little Rock Nine—the first black students to attend Central High School in Little Rock, Arkansas.

On the morning of September 4, 1957, Elizabeth Eckford got up early and pressed the new black-and-white checkered dress her mother had made her for the first day of school. As she was ironing, her little brother turned on the TV. The reporter was wondering if the nine black students knew that there was a mob waiting for them in front of Little Rock Central High School. Well, at least now *she* did.

Elizabeth Eckford

Elizabeth sat down and waited for the adults who were supposed to pick her up and take the six girls and three boys to school. Eight o'clock came. Then 8:15. No one showed up. Since her family had no phone, she had no way of knowing that the adults had changed the pickup plans. Finally, Elizabeth grabbed her notebook and started out the front door toward the bus stop. Her mother called her back into the living room. Together they knelt in prayer. And then Elizabeth left.

The bus let her off a block from Central High. She could see hundreds of white people gathered across the street from her school, <u>restrained</u> by a police barricade. When they spotted her, they started toward her but the police held them back. Soldiers surrounded the giant red brick school. She <u>assumed</u> they were there to help her get inside. As television cameras recorded her every step, she made it to the nearest corner of the school and tried to push through the soldiers to the building. The soldiers refused to let her through. They wouldn't even tell her why.

Gloria Ray
Terrance Roberts
Melba Patillo
Elizabeth Eckford
Ernest Green
MinniJean Brown
Jefferson Thomas
Carlotta Walls
Thelma Motthershed
THE LITTLE ROCK NINE

She tried the main entrance, farther down the block. This time the soldiers moved closer together and crossed their rifles in her face. Then she realized they were there to keep her *out*. With nowhere to go, she stepped back into the street and the mob <u>surged</u> toward her. This time the Little Rock police let them go. Clutching her notebook, she tried to keep

---

Vo•cab•u•lary

restrained (rih STRAYND) kept back
assumed (uh SOOMD) made an educated guess
surged (surjd) moved forward

moving forward toward the bus stop as she was <u>engulfed</u> by the hateful crowd. Some were screaming, "<u>Lynch</u> her!" At one point she looked into the eyes of an old woman. "It seemed a kind face," Elizabeth remembered, "[and then] . . . she spat at me."

Elizabeth made it to a bench by a bus stop and sat down. The crowd closed in. And then, mercifully, the bus pulled up and a <u>sympathetic</u> white woman took her by the arm, led her in, and sat down beside her. The doors closed against the angry faces and the bus pulled away.

For the next three weeks the Arkansas National Guard, under orders from Governor Orval Faubus, kept the nine black students out of school. Finally, a judge ordered the governor to remove the guardsmen from Central High. President Dwight Eisenhower sent one thousand federal troops to Little Rock to protect the six girls and three boys. Each day, the students were picked up by U.S. soldiers who stayed with them until they went in through a side door. **❶**

But there were no troops to protect them when they got inside. "Once we got into the school, it was very dark," recalled Melba Pattillo Beals, another of the nine. "It was like a deep dark castle. And my eyesight had to adjust to the fact that there were people all around me . . . There has never been in my life any stark terror or fear <u>akin</u> to that." All year long they were <u>taunted</u> and tripped, ignored, and called names.

> **❶ Identifying Problem and Solution**
> Who kept the Little Rock Nine out of school for three weeks? Why were they finally able to attend school?

Vo•cab•u•lary

engulfed (en GULFT) swallowed up
lynch (linch) to kill without going through the court system, usually by hanging as by a mob
sympathetic (sim puh THET ik) acting with concern or understanding
akin (uh KIN) similar
taunted (TAWN tid) teased someone to make that person upset or angry

Elizabeth Eckford

"We'd be showering in the gym and someone would turn your shower into <u>scalding</u> . . . you'd be walking out to the volleyball court and someone would break a bottle and trip you on the bottle. I still have scars on my right knee. After a while I started saying to myself, 'Am I less than human?' 'Why did they do this to me?'"

Their parents were terrified. People threatened to kill Elizabeth Eckford's father at work. But the Little Rock Nine didn't quit school, even though some whites refused to attend classes with them. Every one of them finished the year at Central High. Ernest Green, the group's only senior, became the first black student to receive a diploma there.

What Happened to Elizabeth Eckford?

She went to college in Illinois and then returned to Arkansas, where she worked as a substitute teacher in the Little Rock public school system. Like all members of the Little Rock Nine, Elizabeth received the U.S. Congressional Gold Medal in 1997. It is the highest award given to a civilian by the U.S. Congress. ❍

Answering the BIG Question

As you do the following activities, consider the Big Question:
What's fair and what's not?

WRITE TO LEARN Think about the events described in this article. Then write a brief entry in your Learner's Notebook telling what you might have done if you had been in Elizabeth Eckford's shoes on September 4, 1957.

LITERATURE GROUPS In a small group, discuss how the Little Rock Nine helped end racial segregation in schools. Would you be willing to face danger and hardship to right a wrong as the nine students did?

Vo•cab•u•lary

scalding (SCAWL ding) very hot; burning

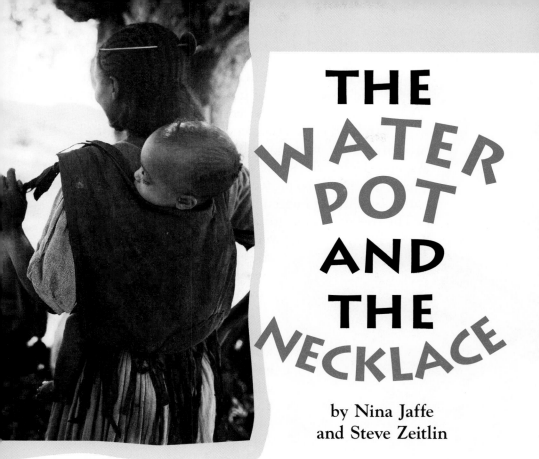

THE WATER POT AND THE NECKLACE

by Nina Jaffe
and Steve Zeitlin

A chief is faced with a difficult decision: Should an innocent girl be killed in the name of fairness?

Once in a village in Nigeria there lived two young girls. Their names were Ashabi and Alaté, and they were the best of friends. They grew up together and married two men from the same village. One day, Ashabi found a <u>kola nut</u> and planted it. The kola tree began to bear fruit, but animals from the village came to eat the leaves and nibble at its roots. Ashabi loved the tree very much, and she wanted to keep it safe.

Vo•cab•u•lary

kola nut (KOH lah nut) a nutlike seed used to make beverages

Then Alaté found a water pot. The bottom had broken off, but it had no other cracks or scratches. It was perfectly round and open on both ends. Alaté could put her arm right through it. That afternoon, she gave the water pot to Ashabi. "Here," she said, "you can put this over your tree. Now it will be protected from the animals and insects." Ashabi hugged her friend and thanked her. The tree grew now, for Ashabi loved and cared for it well. By selling the kola nuts, she even began to <u>acquire</u> some wealth and possessions of her own.

As time passed, Alaté began to look at her friend with envy. "Ashabi will soon be the wealthiest woman in the village!" she thought to herself. So she came before Ashabi and said, "I want the top of my water pot back. Please give it to me." Ashabi replied, "I would be happy to give it back to you, but I can't do that without cutting down the tree."

"Still," said Alaté, "that is my water pot and I want it back—just as it was—with no cracks or scratches on it." **❶** They brought the matter before the chief. He listened and then he ruled: "The pot first belonged to Alaté, who gave it to you. It must be returned."

So Ashabi had to cut down the tree. She grieved for it bitterly.

❶ Inferring
Why do you think Alaté wants her friend to return the pot?

Vo·cab·u·lary

acquire (uh KWY ur) obtain, get, or build up

A year later, Alaté gave birth to her first child, a daughter. On her naming day, Ashabi went to her friend's house and gave the baby a gift, a necklace made of a single piece of brass that was molded to fit her neck perfectly. Alaté thanked her and put the necklace on the child. The girl grew up, and when she was ten years old, Ashabi came before Alaté and said, "I want my necklace back. Please give it to me." Alaté replied, "But my daughter wears the necklace every day."

Ashabi said, "Still, it is mine, and I want it back, just as I gave it to you—whole, with no marks on it." Alaté moaned, "But the child has grown. I can't give it back to you without cutting off my daughter's head!" So they took the matter before the chief.

The chief was a wise man, familiar with the wisdom of the elders and his <u>ancestors</u>. He remembered what happened years before with Ashabi's kola nut tree, and how Alaté had demanded her pot back, causing the death of the tree. Now the two women had come before him again, with the question of Ashabi's necklace. ❷

The chief <u>devised</u> a plan. He called the man who <u>conducted</u> the executions into his tent, and explained the situation and what he wanted him to do. Then he called the two women together.

❷ **Identifying Problem and Solution**
How would you decide this matter?

"Yes," he said, "Ashabi is just in her claim. If Alaté could force Ashabi to cut down the kola tree to reclaim her water pot, then Ashabi can force Alaté to put her daughter to death so that she may reclaim her necklace. Cut off her head!" the chief declared solemnly. The executioner lifted up his ax and held it to the skies, his arms frozen like a statue. Suddenly, tears sprang to Ashabi's eyes. She

Vo•cab•u•lary

ancestors (AN ses turs) members of someone's family who lived before that person
devised (dih VYZD) thought up
conducted (kun DUK tid) carried out

leaped forward and put her arms around the child. "Please don't kill her," she cried. "I was angry about my kola nut tree, but it is not the child's fault. No, I do not want to return bad for bad, for only more bad will come of it. Please let her go." The chief nodded, and the executioner lowered his ax to the ground.

So the child was saved.

In time, the two women who had always been friends could be seen walking through the village with Alaté's daughter between them, selling nuts from a kola tree they had planted together. ○

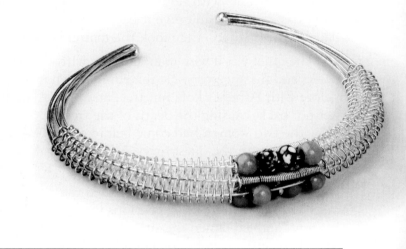

Answering the BIG Question

As you do the following activities, consider the Big Question: **What's fair and what's not?**

WRITE TO LEARN Think about Alaté's feelings of envy as she watched her friend get rich. Has envy ever harmed your relationship with a friend? Write about it in a brief entry in your Learner's Notebook.

PARTNER TALK Meet with a partner who has read "The Water Pot and the Necklace." Discuss these questions: Is it ever fair to give a gift to someone and then demand it back later on? What if the person is unable to return the item?

THEO and RUSTBUCKET

by Doug Holgate

It takes an emergency to make two boys realize what really matters.

WHOA! RUSTY I GOT A *BITE!*

HOOOEEEE!! FEELS LIKE A *BIGGUN!!!*

UGH!...UM, A LITTLE HELP RUSTY- HE'S GUNNA GIT AWAY!

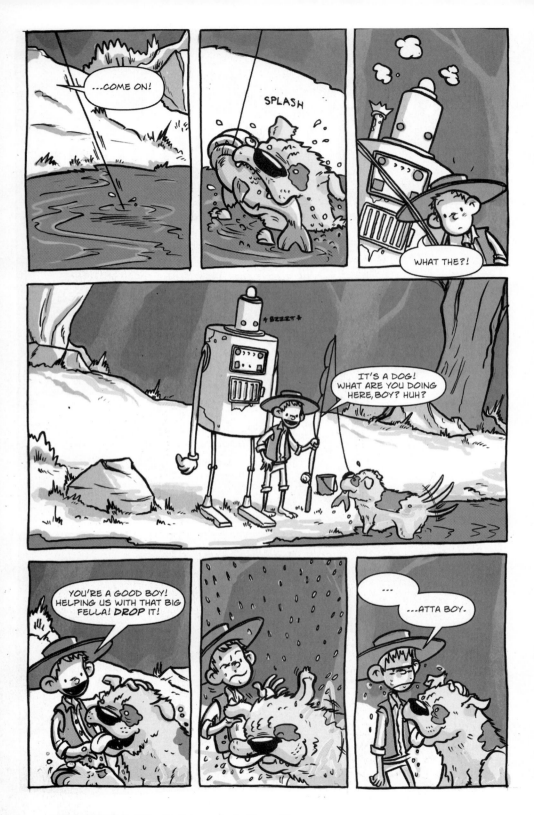

173

177

WRITE TO LEARN

Is Bullseye a fair trade for Theo's lost friend Rustbucket? Why or why not? Write your answer in your Learner's Notebook. Be sure to include your reasons.

Farah Ahmedi:
an *Afghan girl shares the story of her life*

Can something good come out of a horrible accident?

Meet Farah Ahmedi. The 17-year-old Afghan teen and high school senior who lives just outside Chicago recently won the *Good Morning America* and Simon & Schuster "The Story of My Life" contest.

Farah Ahmedi

Last April, Farah's moving life story about her childhood in war-torn Afghanistan and her journey to America in 2002 was voted number one of 6,000 entries by a panel of celebrity authors and more than 18,000 viewers of *Good Morning America*. Soon after winning the contest, her experiences were published in a book, *The Story of My Life: An Afghan Girl on the Other Side of the Sky*.

The book was written in an "as told to" format. This means that Farah was interviewed in her native language, Farsi, by writer Tamim Ansary, who then translated her story into a first-person narrative exactly as she had told it to him.

Here is an excerpt from the memoir that the *Los Angeles Times* calls "the world's most <u>literate</u> reality show."

୬

On that fateful morning I woke up and felt the sun in my eyes. . . .

That light shining in my eyes told me I was late. . . . It was eight o'clock. Class had already started, and I was missing precious minutes of my teacher's stories.

I jumped out of bed. In Kabul a schoolgirl wears a black dress with white stockings and a white head scarf. I threw on this uniform as quickly as I could. I did not have time to pull on the stockings. They were too much trouble. . . . As for my long hair, I didn't have time to comb it. I just left it tangled and unruly from sleep, grabbed my school box, and rushed out the door, forgoing my usual morning bread and tea—I had no time. . . .

And so I thought, I'll take a shortcut today.

By veering off the paved street and cutting across an overgrown brush-filled field directly to the main road that led to my school, I could save two or three minutes. I think that most people knew to stay out of this particular field. . . . I didn't see any warnings posted, but then, I wasn't looking. I was late to school, and that's all I could think about. I started across the field.

Vo•cab•u•lary

literate (LIT ur it) similar to literature

And then suddenly a fire flashed in my face and the earth seemed to move beneath my feet. I remember a shower of soil and then nothing.

I woke up on the ground, surrounded by a crowd. . . . They were all staring down at me with huge eyes. The color had fled from their faces. They looked horrified. Their lips were moving, but I could hear no voices. All I heard was a loud ringing in my ears. The sun blazed down on me, but shadows kept cutting across the light as people pushed their way into the ring of <u>spectators</u>. They just let me lie there for half an hour or more. . . . They didn't know what to do. They didn't know who I was. At that moment, I didn't quite know who I was either. I could feel a strange anxiety gnawing away inside me: I was late for school. . . . I had to get up. But the sight of all the horrified faces buried that anxiety in <u>chaotic</u> panic. I tried to look down at my legs, but I couldn't. It was so confusing. I didn't know what had happened or why I couldn't get up. I felt no pain, . . . just mental <u>turmoil</u> and fear. Those horrified people standing over me were arguing. Was it too late? . . . Should they lift me up? How? The babble of their voices was beginning to come through the ringing now, as they <u>loomed</u> over me, shadowy faces and figures, sunlight twinkling through the shifting spaces between them. ❶

❶ Clarifying
What did Farah see and hear when she woke up?

And then at last I found my voice. "What happened?" I screamed. "Why are you standing there? Pick me up!"

But no one moved to help me. They just crowded against one another, <u>jostling</u> for position and craning over one another's shoulders for a better view of me. . . . I wasn't wearing stockings. I remembered that suddenly.

Vo•cab•u•lary

spectators (SPEK tay turz) people who watch an event
chaotic (kay AW tik) very disorderly and confusing
turmoil (TUR moyl) great commotion or state of great disorder
loomed (loomd) appeared
jostling (JOS ling) bumping or pushing roughly

Stockings took too long to pull on, so I had just slipped on a pair of baggy <u>pantaloons</u> that morning, under my black school dress. And suddenly I knew that those pantaloons were gone. Nothing was left of them except the elastic around my waist. That single fact flooded through me, overwhelming all my senses for an instant. My trousers gone and people gawking at me! . . .

At that moment a man leaned over me. I knew him. He was our neighbor. . . . He came over for a look and recognized me. That good fellow had a patoo, a large shawl that Afghans wear over their shoulders for warmth. With great tenderness, he spread that patoo over my shivering body.

It was he who sent someone to notify my family. . . . My mother came running, howling with dismay. . . .

Afghan women looking at replicas of land mines

Vo•cab•u•lary

pantaloons (pan tuh LOONS) a type of pants

Meanwhile, our neighbor had hailed a taxi. He and the taxi driver rolled me onto the patoo and lifted that blanket by the corners. I don't know what would have happened if that neighbor had not come along. . . .

He and my mother got into the cab with me, and the driver took off. I still couldn't look down at my legs. It's not that I couldn't lift my head. I had the physical strength, but I lacked the will. . . . I began trying to force myself to sneak a glance down there. . . . Finally, I caught one quick glimpse, just one glimpse, and oh my God! That wasn't my leg anymore, it was just meat! Oh, the redness of it, the utter redness. Akh!

And still I felt no pain. When they lifted me out of the taxi, I screamed, but not from pain. I screamed because I knew. It was knowing that forced such sounds out of my throat. . . . **2** When we got to the hospital, they loaded me onto a cart of some kind, rushed me indoors, and put me on a table. There, such a <u>stench</u> of blood and rot <u>assaulted</u> my nose, I couldn't breathe. I was choking. I said to myself, "This is it. I'm going to die. The end has come." The scene before me turned black. I slipped out of the world and for some time, blessedly, knew nothing about anything. . . .

2 Inferring
What did Farah know that made her scream?

When I came to, I felt as if a mountain had been loaded onto one of my legs. . . . That's what the pain felt like: weight. Pure weight. I said to my mother, "What have you put on my leg? It's too heavy, get it off!"

The next day, finally, [doctors] lifted me onto a cart to take me to the bandage-changing room. At that point I gathered my courage and took a long look at my legs. I saw that they were <u>mangled</u>. My family, running alongside my cart, now told me what had happened. "You stepped on a land mine." . . .

Vo•cab•u•lary

stench (stench) a strong, unpleasant smell
assaulted (uh SAWL tud) attacked
mangled (MANG guld) destroyed by cutting, tearing, or crushing

As a child, gazing at the high walls around our home compound, I longed to see what lay on the other side of my city. I never dreamed that I would see our home reduced to <u>rubble</u> and would end up living on the other side of the world, in the suburbs of a city called Chicago.

But in the end, I have decided to tell this story because it is not mine alone. It is the story of many people . . . who have stepped on land mines, [who have] gotten hurt by war, lost their families, fled their homes. Each of us has a story. What happened to me— both the bad and the good—really does happen to people. ❸

❸ Identifying Problem and Solution
What problems does Farah hope to address by telling her story?

I say "the bad and the good" because out of my losses have come tremendous gifts as well. Looking back, I see that my life could have ended so many times, except for unexpected strangers who reached out to me in loving kindness. After I lost my leg, I thought I could never know happiness again, and yet that very loss opened the world to me in strange ways and showed me wonders that I had never imagined.

I have seen my dreams crushed, but new ones have sprouted in their place. . . . I have lost loved ones but not love itself. That's what my story is about. That's the story I want to share with you now, the story of my life, so far.

Life after the Book

Farah Ahmedi was recently named Youth Ambassador for Adopt-A-Minefield's (*www.landmines.org*) student-led campaign to raise awareness about land mines. How else has her life changed since the publication of the book? *Writing* caught up with her to find out.

Vo•cab•u•lary

rubble (RUB ul) broken pieces, such as of bricks or rocks

Writing: After writing the book, what has your experience been at your high school?

Farah: My school has really supported me throughout all this. When the story first came on *Good Morning America* and people were asked to vote for the top three stories that they want to see published in a book, many of my classmates voted for me. After that, they started coming up to me and talking, and saying "hi" and smiling. They were proud of me. I've started making some friends—it's easier for them and for me now to build a friendship.

Writing: You've lived in so many places. What does home mean to you now?

Farah: Home means to me America. When I came to America, I felt like this is it. This is home. I can get my education and do anything I want to do. I can set more goals and dreams. I can do anything. I now have hope—a lot of it.

Writing: What is the best part of America?

Farah: The best part of America is freedom. Men and women have equality. They have so much respect here for women! And, then, you have choices for your career and education. . . . There are so many people from all over the world and there's no problem about what religion you are. It doesn't matter. You can worship the way you want and express yourself. That's the best part.

Writing: What is your least favorite part of America?

Farah: I would like to see Americans pay attention to immigrants and refugees. They don't have to come and give us money and clothes or stuff. They can just volunteer and spend time with us. Maybe teach English or help with transportation. . . .

There's a large immigrant population at my high school. All day, we sit in school and we hear English, but we don't have anyone to speak back to. That's why we have an accent. So if we have an opportunity to speak English with someone, maybe we won't have an accent. . . . At my high school, we've just started

---

Vo·cab·u·lary

immigrants (IM ih grintz) people who come to a country to live planning a multicultural club that anyone, even Americans, can join. They can just come and talk to refugees and immigrants. Maybe through this club, we can come together. It's nice for American kids, too, to learn about Arab [and] other cultures. **4**

4 Distinguishing Fact from Opinion

In this sentence, is Farah stating a fact or giving her opinion?

Writing: Why did you feel it was important to tell your story?

Farah: My story is not just about me. It's all about refugees and immigrants who come [to America] from other countries. We come here to have peace, a safe life, and a good life.

Writing: In telling your story, you had to remember many painful memories. What was that like?

Farah: It is good to remember all the good and bad stuff because those memories help you go ahead. You look back and you say, "Yes, those were bad things." But [they] happened, [and] I want to go ahead. I used to hold on to [my memories] a lot, and I was depressed, but then I said to myself: "Life is not fair— I know that—and life doesn't go back. I want to move ahead." So I moved ahead. ○

Answering the BIG Question

As you do the following activities, consider the Big Question:
What's fair and what's not?

WRITE TO LEARN Farah says, "Life is not fair . . . and life doesn't go back. I want to move ahead." What is your reaction to these words? Jot down your thoughts in your Learner's Notebook.

PARTNER TALK Meet with another student who has read this article. Discuss how Farah responded to her accident. Does it surprise you that she has been able to find "both the bad and the good" in the experience?

MOTHER DOESN'T WANT A DOG

by Judith Viorst

What pet would you most like to have?

Mother doesn't want a dog.
Mother says they smell,
And never sit when you say sit,
Or even when you yell.
And when you come home late at night
And there is ice and snow,
You have to go back out because
The dumb dog has to go.

Mother doesn't want a dog.
Mother says they shed,
And always let the strangers in
And bark at friends instead,
And do disgraceful things on rugs,
And track mud on the floor,
And flop upon your bed at night
And snore their doggy snore.

Mother doesn't want a dog.
She's making a mistake.
Because, more than a dog, I think
She might not want this snake. ❶

> ❶ **Identifying Problem and Solution**
> What is the speaker's solution to the problem?

MERRY-GO-ROUND

by Langston Hughes

What's a child to do when he doesn't know the rules?

Colored child at carnival

Where is the Jim Crow[1] section
On this merry-go-round,
Mister, cause I want to ride?
Down South where I come from
White and colored
Can't sit side by side.
Down South on the train
There's a Jim Crow car.
On the bus we're put in the back—
But there ain't no back
To a merry-go-round!
Where's the horse
For a kid that's black? **2** ○

> **2 Identifying Problem and Solution**
> Why does the child wonder where he can sit on the merry-go-round?

Answering the **BIG** Question

As you do the following activities, consider the Big Question:
What's fair and what's not?

WRITE TO LEARN Think about the two pets mentioned in "Mother Doesn't Want a Dog." Write a brief entry in your Learner's Notebook telling which of these pets you would most like to have. Explain your choice.

LITERATURE GROUPS In a small group, discuss the situation faced by the child in "Merry-Go-Round." Talk about what it must have been like to live in a time when Jim Crow laws were in effect. What might you have done to get rid of those laws?

. . . .
[1] Jim Crow is a term used to describe laws in the South through the mid-1900s that were intended to keep blacks and whites separate.

Cheating:
Excuses, Excuses

Who loses the most when a person cheats?

Most kids who cheat in school know that cheating is wrong. But because they don't want to think of themselves as "cheaters," they come up with a whole bunch of reasons why they have to cheat. Let's take a look at some of the popular ones: ❶

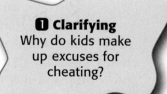

❶ **Clarifying**
Why do kids make up excuses for cheating?

The Excuse: School is hard.

"All my classes are totally hard, and I can't keep up. If I don't cheat, my grades will be terrible."

Why It's Lame:

School isn't supposed to be easy. If you already knew all the answers, you wouldn't actually learn anything. If you try your best and the material still seems way harder for you than anybody else, it's time to talk to your teacher, counselor, or parent. Cheating to get better grades will just hide the problem and, in the long run, just make school even more difficult.

The Excuse: School is unfair.

"Other kids have advantages over me. Some are smart, some are teacher's pets, and some even get private tutors. The only way I can get the same grades is to cheat sometimes."

Why It's Lame:

Yep, some kids make it all look easy, and that can seem unfair. But cheating is just another way of being unfair, isn't it? Let's say that you're the high scorer on your school's basketball team. Another kid sees you making it look easy, and thinks this gives her an excuse to cheat. You'd be angry, right? Breaking the rules is not the way to even things up. **2**

2 Clarifying
Why is cheating to even the odds wrong?

The Excuse: Everybody's doing it.

"Cheating is no big deal because all the kids do it, and only the ones who are obvious get caught."

Why It's Lame:

People—kids *and* adults—do all sorts of things because they think everyone else does them, like taking towels from hotel rooms or driving through "Stop" signs. However, the fact that a lot of people do it and don't get caught doesn't make it any less wrong. Cheating is against the rules for very good reasons, and the fact that someone else did it and got away with it doesn't change this. Try to make your own decisions about what's right and wrong, and stay true to them.

The Excuse: It's cheating only if you do it on tests.

"My friends and I give each other the answers on homework and other stuff we do in class. It's not the same as cheating on a test."

Why It's Lame:

Homework and class projects are important ways to learn, and all students are supposed to finish their work on their own.

Cheating on tests is one kind of cheating, but it's not the only kind. Any time you copy someone else's work or take credit for something you didn't do, it's still cheating, and it's still wrong.

The Excuse: It's not cheating, it's teamwork.

"We're supposed to cooperate with other kids, right? So why can't we work together and trade answers?"

Why It's Lame:

Sometimes teachers will assign group projects where you work with other students. But most assignments are supposed to be done by each student on his or her own, because this makes sure everyone understands every part of the lesson. If you do only half an assignment, and your friend does the other half, then each of you is learning only half the material, instead of both of you learning all of it. Even on group projects, each student is supposed to work hard, and if somebody ends up doing a lot less, this is a form of cheating.

The Excuse: This subject isn't important.

"I never cheat in my favorite classes, but some classes are just dumb, and the things they teach have nothing to do with my life."

Why It's Lame:

There are only so many hours in the school day, and school boards, teachers, and parents work hard to make sure the subjects that get taught are the most important ones. There may be classes that you don't like or that don't come as easy to you, but this doesn't mean that the lessons aren't important. Getting a complete and well-rounded education means learning all kinds of different things, and you can't learn if you cheat.

The Excuse: I don't like my teacher.

"I don't like my teacher, and I don't think he likes me. So I just think it's okay to cheat in his class."

Why It's Lame:

Your feelings about your teacher shouldn't have anything to do with how you do your assignments and take tests. Although

it's great to have a teacher that you like, the main job of a teacher is to help you learn, and you're expected to do your work and not cheat no matter who your teacher is. If you're having a real conflict with a teacher and it's affecting your attitudes about schoolwork, talk to a trusted adult about what's going on.

The Excuse: I don't have time to study.

"I'm stressed for time every day. When I cheat, it's only because I've got so much going on that there's no time left to study."

Why It's Lame:

If you don't have enough time to study, consider cutting back on your other activities, not your schoolwork. Like it or not, school is meant to be your top priority, and if other interests are taking too much time and energy away from it, things probably have to change. Ask a parent to help you rearrange your schedule so you have enough time for schoolwork every single day.

Vo•cab•u•lary

priority (pry OR ih tee) something of high importance

The Excuse: My parents expect perfect grades.

"My mom and dad put soooo much pressure on me about grades; they complain when I get B's and C's. I need A's. So I cheat."

Why It's Lame:

Most parents want their kids to get good grades because of what the grades represent: working hard and learning. In other words, it's *earning* the grade, not the grade itself, that's important. If you're having trouble earning the grades a parent expects of you, consider talking to her or him about what it would take to do better, including more time set aside for homework or outside tutoring. If you feel your parent's expectations are too high or putting too much pressure on you, you may want to discuss this with him or her, or with a school counselor. **3** ○

> **3 Identifying Problem and Solution**
> What are two possible solutions for kids who blame their cheating on parental pressure?

Answering the **BIG** Question

As you do the following activities, consider the Big Question:
What's fair and what's not?

WRITE TO LEARN Think about the excuses for cheating given in this article. Then write a brief entry in your Learner's Notebook giving your opinion of one of the excuses.

PARTNER TALK Meet with another student who has read this selection. Discuss what you think schools can do to help students stop cheating. Do you think most students who cheat would like to stop?

What a Wish!

by Qyzra Walji
and Sandy Fertman Ryan

Physical limitations make a difference in a person's life, but do they make a difference in who a person is?

In all of Qyzra Walji's 13 years, very few of her wishes have been granted. So when the Make-A-Wish Foundation and *Girl's Life* got together to make this shining-star-of-a-girl's dream come true, Qyzra was more than ready for her close-up. Her lifelong goal? To be featured in *Girl's Life* so she could share her message of hope with you.

I guess I'm like any other 13-year-old. I paint my nails, go to the mall, and am very particular about how I dress and wear my hair. I love *The OC* and Ashanti. I also love to daydream. But what I dream about most is that I will one day be able to walk and talk.

At 8 months old, I was diagnosed with <u>cerebral palsy</u>. CP is a condition caused by damage to part of my brain when I was really tiny. The damage interferes with my brain's ability to control my posture and how I move. I'm unable to speak <u>articulately</u>, but I can make sounds. I communicate by using my left hand on a computerized picture board and by typing with one finger on Intellikeys®[1], which is like a typewriter. **❶**

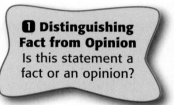

❶ Distinguishing Fact from Opinion
Is this statement a fact or an opinion?

The hardest thing about growing up with CP is seeing other kids do things I can't do. I love soccer and cheerleading, but I'll never be able to participate. I remember watching *Bring It On* and being upset that I couldn't dance like that. But I can move my shoulders to the music, and I'm grateful for that.

The Big Move

I lived in Tanzania, Africa, until I was 6, but I don't remember much about it. My mom says my needs couldn't be taken care of in Tanzania—there are no wheelchairs or disabled-<u>accessible</u> buildings, no classes for kids like me, no physical therapy, and no special bathrooms or showers (which I have to use). The hospitals are filthy, and patients have to wait days or months for medical

....

[1]Intellikeys is a programmable alternative keyboard.

Vo•cab•u•lary

cerebral palsy (SER uh brul PAWL see) a disorder that often results in poor coordination, learning disabilities, and speech difficulties
articulately (ar TIK yuh lut lee) in a clear way
accessible (ak SES uh bul) able to be entered or approached

attention. Even worse, if something had happened to my parents, I would have become a beggar. Tanzanians believe people with special needs—disabilities or limitations—are cursed or have bad spirits inside of them. Their thinking is really backward.

My parents wanted to do all they could for me, so we moved to Canada. I love it here in Ontario—there are lots of places that help people like me. But I hate the cold since I'm small and have to wear a lot of clothes to stay warm. Otherwise, I could easily get very ill.

Although I don't recall much about Tanzania, I do remember that nobody played with me. Everyone just stared. My mom had to push me in a stroller or carry me because I couldn't walk. Kids said things to me like, "You're yucky."

When I moved to Canada and got a wheelchair, I truly understood how different I was from other kids. I was happy to be <u>mobile</u>, but it made it so much more obvious. Most kids are very nice, but there are always some who say mean things like, "Oh, look at that big girl drooling!" (another thing I can't control). Maybe they think I don't understand, but I do and it crushes me.

My mom always says, "Some kids are normal, some are like you, and some are worse off than you. Whatever we are, we are. There's no reason to be ashamed because we all come from God, and He knows what's best for us." When she reminds me of that, I feel better.

Standing Tall

At age 10, I started attending a day camp for kids like me and really gained confidence. For the first time, I didn't feel different. That was the greatest feeling. The volunteers and staff made me realize I could do whatever I wanted. That's also when I received my first computer, which made it much easier to communicate. In fact, it changed my life and helped me get stronger as a person. ❷

> ❷ **Identifying Problem and Solution**
> What problems did day camp help solve?

Vo•cab•u•lary

mobile (MOH bul) able to move

Even though my life can be pretty hard at times, I hate it when people say, "Poor little girl!" It makes me feel down. What helps is when people encourage me, such as when I do my homework well and they say, "Wow, you did such a good job!" That gives me courage to do more. Between my parents, the day camp staff, and people at our church, I get a lot of encouragement. Then, there are my friends—some "normal" and some with special needs. I love hanging with them. We flip through magazines together—my favorite thing to do—for hours, and they do my hair and makeup.

I accept who I am, but I get angry sometimes. Like, when I ask my mom with hand signals for something and she doesn't understand me, I get upset. My mind works quickly, and I want to communicate as fast as I'm thinking but can't. I'm challenged physically, not mentally, but most people don't get that. They assume I'm mentally impaired, but I'm not. That's hard. **3**

3 Inferring
Why do people have a hard time understanding that Qyzra is not mentally impaired?

I love school so much that I'd go on Saturdays if I could. I've always loved learning and, of course, seeing my friends. But about a year and a half after starting school in Ontario, I had to quit for two major hip surgeries. I was so scared. My hips had <u>dislocated</u> due to improper sitting equipment in Tanzania. I was left with casts on both legs for six months. But my friends visited often, so it wasn't too bad.

Just a Regular Teen

I'm totally into boys. I have a crush on my neighbor (don't tell!), and I can't help smiling when I see him. I can't imagine ever getting married, but I'd love to have a boyfriend someday.

Still, at times I think, "I'm 13, and this is so unfair!" When I feel that way, I don't want to do anything. I pull myself out of the

Vo•cab•u•lary

dislocated (DIS loh kay tud) moved out of position

mood by watching a funny movie. Once I laugh, I'm OK.

Most frustrating, though, is having everything done for me. I have to be fed, bathed, dressed, and changed every day. Imagine your mom changing you like a baby. It's not fun. But my parents are amazing, so I deal . . . and try to keep my spirits up.

An Unbreakable Spirit

Helping other kids with hardships really makes me happy. When Hurricane Katrina hit, I had my father send cans of food.

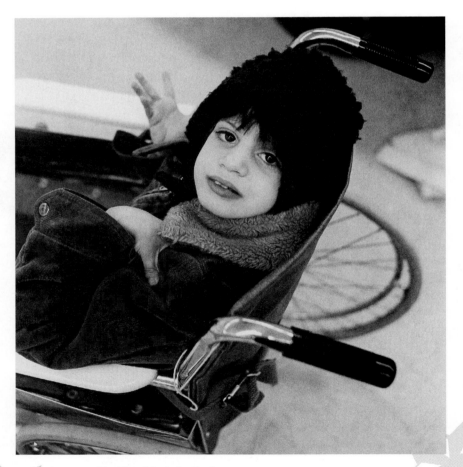

A young girl with mild cerebral palsy

I hate seeing anyone suffer. I'd love to be a <u>mentor</u> to kids with special needs. I want to set an example for them, and that's very motivating to me, especially when I feel down.

I want kids to realize that, if you have a disability or illness, you should never give up on life. Never be ashamed of who you are, and realize you are very special. Never say you can't do something. Always say you can—because you can! My wish to the Make-A-Wish Foundation was to be in *GL* magazine because all of my favorite actresses are in it. I figured, "Why can't I be in it, too?" And here I am. So you really can do whatever you want to if you put your mind to it. **4**

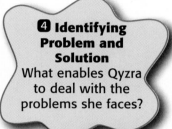

4 Identifying Problem and Solution
What enables Qyzra to deal with the problems she faces?

Even though I can't talk, walk, or write, it's amazing that people can still get to know who I am. I have really good eye gestures, and that's how people read me. Maybe since I have something that limits me, I was given other "powers," like a big smile, to make up for it. So even if you are upset or have problems, keep smiling, like I do, and everything will be fine. ○

Answering the BIG Question

As you do the following activities, consider the Big Question: **What's fair and what's not?**

WRITE TO LEARN Think about how Qyzra describes her life. What have you learned about what it is like to live with cerebral palsy? Write your response in your Learner's Notebook.

PARTNER TALK Meet with another student who has read this article. Brainstorm a list of all the things you have in common with Qyzra.

Vo·cab·u·lary

mentor (MEN tor) teacher

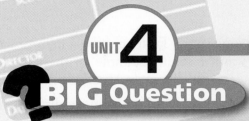

What makes you who you are?

With so many outside influences around you—family, friends, society—you may wonder how much power you have to decide who you are. As you read the following selections, think about the question:
What makes you who you are?

As you read the selections in this unit, apply these reading skills.

- **Visualizing** Create pictures in your mind as you read.
- **Responding** React in a personal way to what you read. Tell what you like, dislike, or find interesting or surprising.
- **Interpreting** Use your own knowledge and the clues in the selection to decide what the events or ideas mean.
- **Monitoring Comprehension** Pause from time to time to make sure you understand what you are reading.

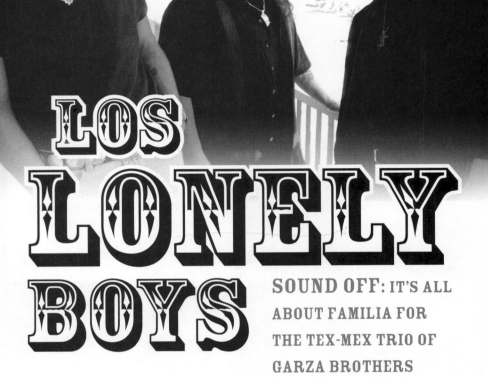

LOS LONELY BOYS

SOUND OFF: IT'S ALL ABOUT FAMILIA FOR THE TEX-MEX TRIO OF GARZA BROTHERS

by Ron Arias and
JoJo, Henry, and Ringo Garza

On the Band's Name

"Our father [Henry] wrote a song for us when we were kids called 'Lonely Boy,'" says Ringo. At the time, "we were singing at a restaurant. We weren't even getting paid money; we were getting food. And our dad told us we've got to have a name. So we called ourselves Los Lonely Boys."

On the Family Business

"Our father and his brothers played music when they were young too," says Henry. Says JoJo: "Music has been with us since we were born. Our father gave us guidance, and our mother [Maria] gave us love. And she sings beautifully."

On Overcoming Tragedy

"When I was 18 my wife and I had a son who passed away from SIDS [sudden infant death syndrome] when he was 5 months old," says Henry. "That was a big part of Los Lonely Boys. It affected all of us." Adds Ringo: "We could hear Henry crying on the guitar." Says Henry: "And my brothers, they cried right back."

On Their Next Album

"Sometime next year," says JoJo. "We have to live through life some more. Something has to inspire you, feeling bad or feeling good, and that's when it comes."

On Their Dream

"We want to set a good example for the human race—not just Chicanos or Americanos or whatever," Henry says. "We're making music for everyone." ○

Answering the BIG Question

As you do the following activities, consider the Big Question:
What makes you who you are?

WRITE TO LEARN Think about how the Garza brothers were influenced by their parents. Write a brief entry in your Learner's Notebook about the influence that family members have had on your life.

LITERATURE GROUPS Meet with two or three others who have read this selection. Discuss what JoJo says about the group's next album. Why isn't the group ready to release a new album yet?

Pig Brains

by Alden R. Carter

Some people use their brains to solve their problems. They are just that smart.

I was headed for the outside doors and the fall afternoon when a voice behind me boomed, "Hey, Shadis!"

I turned, smile fixed, <u>resigned</u> to taking the usual load of garbage from my favorite <u>Neanderthal</u>: the Doughnut. Now, Doughnut's a big guy, about six four and maybe 260, making him

---

Vo•cab•u•lary

resigned (rih ZYND) accepting of something that cannot be avoided
Neanderthal (nee AN dur thawl) primitive man

a foot taller and about 120 pounds fatter than I am. Fortunately, the brain that knocks around inside his massive skull is inversely proportional[1] to his overall size. ❶ Put another way, I'm twice as smart. Which is handy. "Hey Doughnut," I said.

❶ **Visualizing**
Picture the two boys standing side by side.

He flopped a python-thick arm around my shoulders.

"When you coming out for football, Donny? I could use a blocking dummy." He guffawed. Nitwit.

"Maybe next year," I said, and changed the subject. "What are you bringing to O'Brien's class tomorrow?"

"Huh?" he said.

"Food, Doughnut. We're supposed to bring something that reflects our <u>ethnic</u> <u>heritage</u>." *Which in your case is probably raw* <u>*mastodon*</u>, I thought, but didn't say.

"Oh yeah," he said. "I nearly forgot. My ma's going to make some doughnuts. We're German, and Germans eat a lot of doughnuts."

"Do they?" I said, to be polite.

"Yeah. At least my family does." He grabbed a fistful of his belly with <u>typical</u> lineman's pride. "Doughnuts put lead in our pants so we can block better. Coach O'Brien loves how I block. And he loves my mom's doughnuts, too."

"Really?" I said.

"Yep. I brought six dozen to practice just last week. They were

. . . .

[1]The phrase "inversely proportional" here means that although Doughnut's size is very large, his brain is very small.

Vo•cab•u•lary

ethnic (ETH nik) relating to a group of people having a common culture
heritage (HAIR ih tij) what is worthy of being saved over generations
mastodon (MAS tuh don) an extinct, elephantlike animal
typical (TIP ih kul) having the qualities of a certain type

all gone in five minutes."

"Do tell?" I said.

"Yep. So, who else is bringing food tomorrow?"

"It's you, me, and Melinda Riolo this week."

"Melinda? Hey, you kinda liked her last year, didn't you?"

"She's okay," I said.

"I think she thinks you're a nerd." He laughed.

Well she thinks you're a baboon! So we're even, jerk. "Makes no difference to me," I said.

He grinned, knowing better. "Yeah, right. So, what are you bringing?"

"Brains," I said. "Lithuanians eat a lot of brains."

He stared at me. "You're kidding!"

"Nope. Calf brains, sheep brains, goat brains, all sorts of brains."

He let his arm drop from my shoulder. "That's gross."

"Not really. I like pig brains best. They've got kind of a nutty flavor."

Suddenly his hand was back on my shoulder, and it wasn't friendly. He turned me to face him, his eyes mean. "You're putting the Doughnut on, man. I don't like it when people do that. It's like they think I'm stupid or something."

But you are, Doughnut. You are. I just wish you weren't so big. ❷ "I'm not putting you on, Doughnut. I swear."

He stared at me for a long minute, his hand slowly <u>kneading</u> my shoulder. "If you're lying, you'd better tell me now. I might just hurt you a little bit."

I gave the Boy Scout sign. "I swear,

❷ **Monitoring Comprehension**
Why are these words in italics? Does Donny say them out loud?

Vo·cab·u·lary

kneading (NEED ing) working something with the hands

Doughnut. I'm bringing Lithuanian fried brains."

He grunted, still looking suspicious, and let me go.

I made it to the street on wobbly knees and started to walk home past the grade school and down the hill into the Third Ward. What had I done? If I didn't show up tomorrow with Lithuanian fried brains, I'd better show up with a doggone good excuse. Or else Doughnut was going to hurt me a lot more than a little bit.

The only sane, logical thing to do was to come up with a good excuse. But the more I thought about it, the more I really wanted to bring fried brains. I wanted to gross Doughnut out. I mean, the guy grossed me out just by being alive. Now it was my turn.

There really is a recipe for fried brains in the Lithuanian cookbook my mom has. She wrote away for it last spring so she could make a special dinner for my grandpa's 80th birthday. I helped her pick the menu: "Hey, Mom, here's one we could try. Lithuanian fried brains. Soak the brains overnight in a pan of water in the refrigerator, then—"

"Stop," she said. "I don't want to hear it."

"But, Mom! Maybe he had them growing up. Maybe he's been longing for some fried brains ever since he left Lithuania."

"Believe me, he hasn't. He's a finicky eater. It drove your grandma nuts."

"Aw, Mom—," I whined.

"No brains! Find something else."

By the time I got home the sheer brilliance of my inspiration had produced some blind spots in my usually <u>acute</u> vision. Except for twenty or thirty sound, sane reasons, I couldn't see why I shouldn't bring fried brains. Oh, there were a few <u>complications</u>— like where to get the basic ingredient—but that was minor stuff. I could make this happen.

Vo•cab•u•lary

acute (uh KYOOT) sharp; perceptive
complications (kawm plih KAY shuns) difficulties that make things worse

Pig Brains

I called Lerner's Meat Market and asked if they had any brains. Mr. Lerner laughed. "No, I haven't seen brains on sale in thirty years. Nobody around here cooks brains. Maybe in Albania or someplace, but not central Wisconsin."

"Rats," I muttered.

"Nope, we don't have them, either. You might try Albertson's Supermarket though. They might have rats."

"Ha, ha," I said. "Very funny."

"We try. What do you want the brains for?"

"A science project."

"Oh. Well, you might try the stockyards over in Stuart."

How was I supposed to get to Stuart without a car, a license, or a <u>gullible</u> parent? (My mom was decidedly ungullible, my dad permanently absent without leave.) "Do you suppose Albertson's might have some brains?" I asked.

"You could ask, but I'd bet a thousand-to-one against."

"Thanks, Mr. Lerner."

"Sure enough. Good luck."

I slumped in the chair. No brains, no gross-out of the Doughnut. Rats and double rats. (Or words to that effect.) But the idea wouldn't let go, and I had my second inspiration of the day. Remember the Halloween game where squealing kids pass the pieces of Frankenstein's monster from hand to hand under a sheet: grapes for the eyes, a carrot for the nose, pepper slices for the ears, *spaghetti for the brains*. *Shadis*, I told myself, *you are brilliant*.

I pedaled my mountain bike down to Albertson's and inspected the pasta selections. I finally decided on fettuccine, although I was briefly tempted by some green linguine.

Mom was meeting a <u>client</u> for supper and my sister was

Vo•cab•u•lary

gullible (GUL uh bul) easily tricked into believing something
client (KLY unt) customer

studying at a friend's, so I had the kitchen to myself. Good thing, because making some passable brains out of fettuccine took quite a bit of experimentation. I finally managed what I thought was a pretty good <u>facsimile</u> by cooking the noodles <u>al dente</u>, rolling them in cornmeal, and frying them in some oil. I drained them on paper towels, stuffed them into a loaf pan, and stuck it in the refrigerator.

By then I was on a pretty good roll. *A dip*, I thought. We need some brain dip. I searched the refrigerator and found half a bottle of cocktail sauce. I poured it into a neutral container and wrote "Lithuanian Brain Dip" on a label. Nah, I could do better than that. I tore it off and wrote "Cozzackakus: Blood of the Cossacks." Much better. ❸

Digging in the refrigerator at breakfast the next morning, my sister yelped, "Oh, gross!"

Mom looked over Amy's shoulder. "What on earth?"

"Don't touch," I said. "Social studies project."

"What could this possibly have to do with social studies?" Mom asked.

> ❸ **Responding**
> What's your reaction to Donny's fake pig brains and fake brain dip?

Vo•cab•u•lary

facsimile (fak SIM uh lee) exact copy
al dente (al DEN tay) cooked but still firm when bitten

"Really!" my sister said.

"I meant science," I said. "You don't want to know any more."

"You've got that right," Mom said. "Just get it out of my refrigerator."

By this time the dazzle of my idea had faded considerably and I was having some decidedly unpleasant second thoughts. Playing a joke on Doughnut was dangerous enough, but getting caught by Mr. O'Brien might be even worse. Mr. O'Brien doesn't fit the stereotype of a football coach. He doesn't have a big belly, he doesn't glower a lot, and he doesn't think football is the most important thing in the world. He thinks social studies is. He expects a lot, even from Doughnut, who sits in the back of the class trying to look interested. (Doughnut thinks O'Brien is God. Or just about.)

Mr. O'Brien pegs the needle on his hyper meter at least four or five times a day. He crashes around the room, slapping his pointer on maps, globes, and timelines. He pounds his fist on his desk, climbs on his chair, playacts at being this or that historical figure, even beats his head against the wall if that's what it takes to make a point. In other words, he's a heck of a teacher. But he isn't someone to mess with, and I was beginning to wish I was bringing Lithuanian sponge cake or something. ❹ Maybe I'd tell everybody that I'd brought Lithuanian cornmeal-coated fried noodles. Big delicacy, if you're into that kind of thing. Then I'd lie like crazy to Doughnut and hope that he only broke a couple of my bones.

> ❹ **Interpreting**
> What makes Mr. O'Brien such a good teacher?

Melinda Riolo didn't bother to go to her desk but marched right to the front of the room with her casserole dish. She stood there, tapping her foot, while Mr. O'Brien finished the roll. He smiled at her. "All right, Miss Riolo, go ahead."

Vo•cab•u•lary

stereotype (STAIR ee uh typ) a preset, overly simple idea or image
glower (GLOW ur) have an angry look on one's face

She uncovered the dish and tilted it for everybody to see. "I brought eggplant parmigiana, which I like because it doesn't have a lot of calories. Since I lost all that extra weight last year in junior high, I don't eat a lot of the fattening stuff Italians like. I mean all the cheese and stuff. But this is pretty good. Enjoy." She set down the dish and marched to her desk across the aisle from mine. My heart bumped a couple of times with longing.

Doughnut swaggered to the front. He opened a big plastic pail of greasy sugar doughnuts. "They're really good," he said. "My mom fries 'em in real lard."

Melinda muttered, "Oh, charming. Now they're an extra five hundred calories." She eyed me narrowly. "You're being quiet today. Did you forget to bring something?"

"No, I've got it right here in the bag."

"What is it?"

"Brains," I said.

"You're putting me on!"

I looked at her and couldn't lie. "Yeah, but don't tell anybody else. It could cost me about sixteen broken bones."

Doughnut finished telling how he could put away a dozen doughnuts straight from the boiling deep fryer. "Two dozen if they're small. They don't call me the Doughnut for nothing!" He grinned, using both hands to grab fistfuls of his belly. People laughed, and he swaggered back to his desk.

I took a deep breath, followed it with a short prayer, and stumbled confidently to the front of the class. I whipped the towel from the top of the loaf pan. "Ladies and gentlemen, boys and girls, these are Lithuanian fried brains. They're an old delicacy in traditional Lithuanian homes. When we're up at my grandpa's, we play a lot of <u>pinochle</u>. And while we play, we usually have popcorn, chips, or fried brains."

Vo•cab•u•lary

pinochle (PEE nuk ul) a card game

I prodded at the greasy tangle with a finger. Jeez, it was obvious they were noodles. Even Doughnut must have guessed by now. "It's kind of hard to find brains to fry sometimes. Sheep and goat brains are supposed to be best, but there just aren't many sheep and goats around here. Calf brains are easier to find and they're really good. But I like pig brains best and that's what I brought today."

Up to this point I'd been too nervous to look directly at my classmates. But now I chanced it and was greeted by a lot of open mouths, screwed-up noses, and generally horrified expressions. Doughnut was absolutely gray. **5** Good grief, they believed me! I took a breath and put the <u>accelerator</u> to the floor. "Now, when we get the brains, we soak them overnight in a big pan in the refrigerator. It's kind of a good thing to remember they're in there. Otherwise, the next time you open the refrigerator, it's— *whoa*—Frankenstein's laboratory! But"—I shrugged—"you kind of get used to that sort of thing around my grandpa's house."

5 Visualizing
Imagine the reactions of Donny's classmates.

I dug into the tangle, separated a sticky wad of three or four noodles, and held it up. "The next morning we slice the brain and it falls apart into these sort of floppy wormlike things." (There were some very satisfying groans. Doughnut had gone from gray to ashen.) "We roll them in cornmeal and fry them in oil. We drain them on some paper towels and then put them on the table in a big bowl. Brains are really best served hot, but they're still good cold. Like popcorn's good hot or cold."

I headed the wad of noodles toward my mouth, then pulled it back at the last second. "Whoops, I almost forgot. There's also the dip my mom makes from an old recipe my grandma brought from the old country. It's called *Cozzackakus*, which means "blood of the Cossacks." I asked my grandpa about the name and he said

Vo•cab•u•lary

accelerator (ak SEL uh ray tur) pedal or thing that controls the speed of something

it's because Lithuanians don't like Cossacks, who used to be these real tough bandit types who raided a lot. My grandpa says not even Cossacks like Cossacks that much, so—"

Mr. O'Brien interrupted. "This would be an example of ethnic prejudice, class. As we discussed, many older people have them. Go ahead, Don. This is just great."

"Ah, thanks. Anyway, I'm not sure my grandpa ever actually knew any Cossacks, but that's how the sauce got its name. So here's how you eat pig brains." I dipped the noodles in the shrimp sauce, stuck them in my mouth and chewed. They were terrible, but I grinned. "This is a really good batch. Pig brains are just so much better than calf or beef. Did I mention beef brains? The butchers stopped selling them because people started worrying about mad cow disease. But my grandpa says all Lithuanians are already pretty crazy, so they probably wouldn't get any worse if they caught it. So anyway, who'd like to try some Lithuanian fried brains?"

Nobody moved for a long minute. Then Melinda stood and strode to the front of the class. She gave me a look that was at least half glare. "I bet these are fattening as all get-out."

"I don't know, Melinda. Maybe a little."

She plucked a few noodles from the pan, dipped them in the cocktail sauce, and popped them in her mouth. She chewed and then shrugged. "Not bad. Could use some salt, maybe."

Mr. O'Brien jumped up. "Okay, everybody line up. You know the rule:

Pig Brains

Everybody's got to try everything, unless you've got a genuine, doctor-certified food allergy." He rubbed his hands together. "This is great! Just great. This is what we want. Something unusual. Something really <u>authentic</u>. Come on, everybody. Line up. Paper plates and spoons are right here. Don and Melinda, go ahead. No standing on ceremony here."

When we were back at our desks, Melinda glared at the doughnut on her plate. "I'd rather have brains." She leaned over and started to whisper, "You were kid—"

"Hold on, Doughnut!" Mr. O'Brien shouted. "You missed the brains. No cheating."

Doughnut grinned sheepishly and dug a few noodles from the pan.

"Don't forget the blood sauce, Doughnut," I called. "Makes them even better."

Leaning against his desk, Mr. O'Brien was digging into a big serving of brains. He smacked his lips. "You know, Don. If I didn't know better, I'd swear these were noodles."

I almost choked on a bite of eggplant but managed a weak smile. "Yeah, they're kind of similar, aren't they?"

"Sure are. What do you think, Doughnut?"

Doughnut was sitting at his desk, staring at his plate. He looked up pleadingly at Mr. O'Brien, who gave him a now-be-a-man stare. Doughnut sighed, picked up a shred of brains, and stuck it in his mouth. It was a moment of high drama, but I couldn't help glancing at Melinda to see if she was savoring it as much as I was. That's how I missed Doughnut's bolt for the bathroom. He only made it as far as the tall wastebasket beside the door. And when he let go, it was pretty awesome. The metal can <u>resonated</u> like a kettledrum, magnifying the heave into something truly <u>stupendous</u>—a barf worthy of the Doughnut in all his grossness. The sound and the smell

---

Vo·cab·u·lary

authentic (aw THEN tik) genuine
resonated (REZ uh nayt ed) continued the sound
stupendous (stoo PEN dus) extremely wonderful

set off a chain reaction that sent about a dozen girls and just as many guys out the door and down the hall to the rest rooms. **6**

6 Visualizing
Can you picture the scene described in this paragraph?

Mr. O'Brien stood at the front of the class, hands on his hips, glaring at Doughnut's broad rear end as Doughnut heaved a couple more times. He shook his head. "Well, that's it for today, I guess." He waved a hand at the few of us who still sat frozen in our seats. "The rest of you can go. I've got to get Doughnut cleaned up. Don, Melinda, come get your dishes."

I picked up the half-empty loaf pan and followed Melinda out. At the door I paused. "I'm sorry, Mr. O'Brien."

He slapped me on the shoulder. "Not your fault we've got a bunch of sissies in this class. You did a great job. The most original ethnic dish we've ever had. An A+ all the way. Right, Doughnut?"

Doughnut leaned back on his heels, his face the color of dirty gym socks. "Right, Coach."

"As a matter of fact, we've got a big game Friday night," Mr. O'Brien went on. "Maybe I'll have Don bring a couple of pans of brains by the locker room. Some fried brains and some 'blood of the Cossacks' might be just the thing you boys need to fire up for a game against the conference champions. What do you think, Doughnut?"

Doughnut looked at Mr. O'Brien and then at

me. *I am dead*, I thought. "Right, Coach. I'll do better. I promise. I'll be the first one to take some."

"Darn right you will. Now, are you man enough to take that wastebasket down to the custodian's room and wash it out?"

"Yes, sir."

We watched him <u>trudge</u> down the hall, head hanging. Mr. O'Brien slapped me on the shoulder a final time. "Good work, Shadis. See you tomorrow."

A half block from the school, Melinda was sitting on one of the swings in the playground behind the grade school. "Okay," she said. "What were they really?"

"Fettuccine."

"Yeah, I thought so. Did O'Brien catch on?"

I shrugged. "Who knows? If he did, he decided to go along with the joke."

"You're lucky. You were way out on the edge. What did he say to you?"

"Not much. He said maybe he'd have me bring a couple of pans of brains to the locker room before Friday night's game."

Vo·cab·u·lary

trudge (truj) walk slowly with heavy steps

She laughed. "Cool. I bet half those jocks would lose their lunch. Are you going to do it?"

"Are you kidding? I don't have that kind of death wish. I think pig brains may be real hard to find for the next few weeks."

"And sheep, goat, and calf brains?"

"Them too," I said.

She laughed again. "I'm glad you did it. Took Doughnut down a notch." She grinned at me. "And put you up a couple, even if nobody knows what you really had in that pan but me."

I shrugged. "That's okay. I don't want to be a dead hero. . . . Hey, you walking my way?"

"Yeah, I could do that," she said. "Definitely." **7** ○

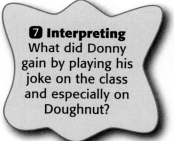

7 Interpreting
What did Donny gain by playing his joke on the class and especially on Doughnut?

Answering the BIG Question

As you do the following activities, consider the Big Question: **What makes you who you are?**

WRITE TO LEARN Think about how Donny uses his brainpower to play a joke on a bully. Can you think of other creative, nonviolent ways to deal with bullies? Jot down your ideas in your Learner's Notebook.

LITERATURE GROUPS Meet with two or three others who have read "Pig Brains." Discuss what you think it takes to become a person who stands up to the bullies of the world. What are the risks and the rewards?

Beavers Busted!

by Deborah Underwood

Each creature is born with certain abilities. What are the natural abilities of beavers?

Need cash? Some Louisiana beavers might be able to float you a loan! When police learned that bags of stolen money totaling U.S. $67,000 had been stashed in a creek, officers went to <u>investigate</u>.

Vo·cab·u·lary

investigate (in VES tuh gayt) make a search to find out the truth

They began tearing down a beaver dam to lower the water level—and discovered hundreds of dollars in loose bills woven in with the dam's tree branches. "The bills were still whole," Major Michael Martin says. "They were just really muddy."

Beavers build dams from wood, but the <u>resourceful</u> rodents will add stones, plants, and even clothing. <u>Apparently</u> the beavers had found one of the money bags at the bottom of the creek, opened it, and used the bills like leaves!

Officers worked until midnight to gather up the loot and then dried the soggy bills in a clothes dryer.

The thieves were caught. The beavers? They repaired the dam by morning. Maybe they should've kept enough cash to hire a carpenter! ❶ ○

> **❶ Responding**
> What information in this article did you find interesting or surprising?

Answering the BIG Question

As you do the following activities, consider the Big Question:
What makes you who you are?

WRITE TO LEARN Think about how beavers are busy, resourceful creatures by nature. Write a brief entry in your Learner's Notebook describing the traits that are part of your nature.

PARTNER TALK Meet with a partner who has read "Beavers Busted." Discuss a variety of human abilities. Which ones are people born with? Which ones have to be learned?

Vo·cab·u·lary

resourceful (rih SORS ful) able to find quick and clever ways to overcome difficulties
apparently (uh PAIR unt lee) clearly

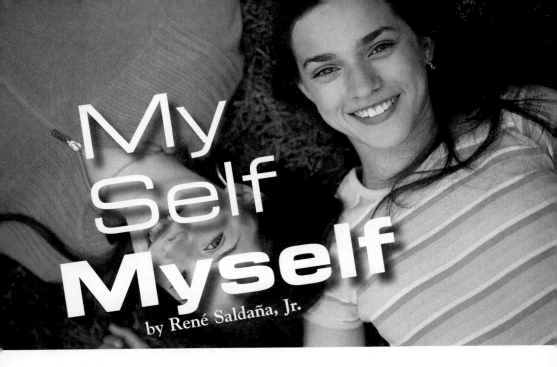

My Self Myself

by René Saldaña, Jr.

Do you think parents treat each of their children the same way?

They're punks—the both of them, always hugging him <u>cozy</u> and patting his back like when he actually was a baby, and whispering in his ear, "Ooh, poor baby, poor thing, are you okay, did she hurt you?"

"I didn't do anything. He did it to himself. Ask him: I didn't even touch the big crybaby," I say to them. I'm on the old, creaky swing set in our backyard. They're sitting on the patio.

My poor excuse for a mother <u>glares</u> at me. My father shakes his head. They think they're doing right by him, but here he is, middle-school age and they treat him like a baby. He'll be a sissyboy if they keep that up.

Vo·cab·u·lary

cozy (KOH zee) having a friendly closeness
glares (glairz) stares in an angry way

My way, he'll know what's what in this world and how to deal with it.

"Hush up, Missy!" my mother says. "You hush up. You've done enough harm already. Just shut up."

You shut it, Mabel, I think, but I don't say it. I know if I do Mabel'll let go of Deuce (that's what my dad calls my brother, not Leonard Junior for being named the same). Then she'll jump up and snag me off the swings; so instead I just think it and keep swinging. She won't hold me in her arms. Dad sometimes does, but not in a good long while. So I've learned my own way. Who needs hugs anyway? ❶

What a baby Dewey is. That's what I call him, and he used to cry about it to Mom and Dad—"Missy's not calling me by my right name, Mommy." So I'd get a good talking-to, Mom sometimes shaking me by the arm and saying, "How can you not get it through your thick skull? Be nice to him. Stop teasing. He's only a boy." So, after our "talk" I'd go back to calling him Deuce, but within a week I'd forget the talking-to and the shaking by the arms and call him Dewey. He'd cry again, and again my parents would call me to their room.

❶ **Responding**
Do you feel sympathy for Missy? Why or why not?

You'd think he wasn't in middle school and a starter on the football team, with his constant whimpering. He just now tried getting into Mom's lap, but he's so heavy that even Mom tells him, "Get off me and sit on the floor, baby; you're too big to be sitting on your mommy." But then she rubs his forehead like he likes, and they go inside to watch TV. I stay outside, swinging. The lightning bugs sparkling.

These last couple of weeks he hasn't complained about me calling him Dewey because some of the guys at school, Franky the quarterback for one, also called him Dewey one day at practice. And now the name is cool, and that's supposed to make Dewey cool too because the guys know his name.

Today, right before he went crying to Mabel and Dad, he and I were in the backyard. I was hammering anthills with a croquet

mallet, and he was piddling around with his latest invention—
a pulley, rigged up to the tree, that's connected to his bedroom
window. Dewey's always trying to invent stuff, but his ideas, even
though he makes them work, serve zero purpose, I mean none
whatsoever. This one seemed it could be good for something, but
what kind of a sister would I be telling him that? Still, I couldn't
help looking at it and thinking it would be perfect for sending
up secret notes, or food, if he were ever grounded and sent to his
room. Like that would ever happen.

This pulley system could only work, though, with two people
operating it. One at the bottom pulling on the ropes and the other
jailed in my brother's room waiting for the secret goods: a plate of food,
a treasure map, or instructions for an escape. So Dewey said to me,
"Hey, Missy, come here, will you? Let's see if this works. Come on."

I dropped the mallet and walked over.

"Okay," he said, "I'm gonna go upstairs, and when I say the
word, you start pulling."

"What are you going to do?"

"I said, I'm going upstairs, and wait."

"Why don't I go upstairs, and you stay down here and do all
the work?"

"It's not work. It's a pulley, duh. It keeps you from having to
work. You would think you'd like a tool like this, that lets you
be all lazy like you are." He laughed. When he wanted to, he
could be a cool kid, like just then, making a crack like he did, but
mostly he whimpered. I had my work cut out.

"Sure, whatever, jerk."

He started for the sliding door, then I asked, "You want me to
pull on it this way?" And I pulled on it.

He ran toward me. "No no no. The other way, stupid. Like
this." You see, a few months ago, he wouldn't've dared call me
stupid. Now it's part of his daily "insult my sister" vocabulary.

I must have jammed the pulley somehow because it wasn't
working now that Dewey was pulling on it hard. "You broke it,"
he said, then I heard a snap, looked up, the pulley came loose,

and bonked Dewey on the shoulder.

He looked at me, then grabbed his shoulder, and I said, "You'll be okay. It was only a bump. You're not going to be a sissy and go crying to Mabel, are you?"

Then he screamed out and started crying. That's when my parents came out to the patio, hugged on him, and said, "Ooh, poor baby."

When Dewey settled down, they went in and turned on the TV.

I'm on the swing now, and I can hear the phony TV people talking, that's how loud my family likes it. Through the window at the kitchen and the sliding door, I see the light of the TV shining on and off.

For the past two weeks, since Dewey went from being a nobody to a somebody because now he's okay with the name Dewey, I've been trying to come up with another name for him that'll bother him like before. ❷ But nothing. Earlier he gave me an idea, though. Right before he got hit with the pulley.

❷ **Monitoring Comprehension**
Why does Missy want to invent a new name for her brother?

In French class, first thing we learned was the numbers: in French, two is *deux*, pronounced "dew," or even "doo," as in "doo-doo," but other people might misunderstand and think I'm calling him Dew and say, "What a nice thing to call your brother.

You must really like him." But I don't; okay, I do, but so what?

I've got a better idea. He'd said, "It's a pulley, duh!" So that's it: Duh.

The sliding door opens, and there he is. "Hey, Sis, Mom and Dad want you to come inside."

"Hey, you know, in French the number two is pronounced 'dew,' but we're not in France, we're in Georgia. I was going to call you Dew, but it just doesn't sound right, so I'm gonna call you Duh instead."

He thinks about it for a moment, and I can't see the lights coming on in his head like people say they can see, just a blank stare. Then, "Maw, Missy's calling me names again."

"Grow up," I tell him.

He leaves the door open, and then I hear it. Mabel's screaming for me to come inside.

Then I say, "But I'm just putting to good use all the stuff I'm learning at school. You should be proud of me like you are of Duh when he invents one of his good-for-nothing <u>contraptions</u> and says he learned it in science class."

"I'll have none of that." Like always, she shakes me by the arm and tells me, "Deuce is young and <u>impressionable</u>. He's at a stage in his life where he could go good or bad depending on all kinds of stuff. I don't even want to think of him doing drugs, failing class, or quitting school. Listen, Missy, you're the grown-up here. You can take care of yourself. Your brother's still, you know, so can you help us out a bit?" **3**

Duh doesn't look at me like he used to when he was little, smiling because I was getting in trouble. He stares at the

3 Responding
Do you think Missy's mother is being unfair to her? Why or why not?

Vo•cab•u•lary

contraptions (kawn TRAP shunz) devices or machines that seem strange

impressionable (im PRESH eh neh buhl) easily influenced

TV instead, then walks out of the room to the kitchen.

"But, Mom," I say.

"No buts, young lady. Apologize to your brother and go up to your room," she says.

And I scream, "I'm sorry for everything, Deuce," then go to my room.

I'll call him that, but when the shaking wears off, it'll be back to Duh. I close the door behind me. I lie down on the bed and wonder, looking up at my blank ceiling, Who's worried about what path I take? What about my self-esteem?

I'll worry about my self myself.

There's a knock at the door. It's Duh, and he says, "Hey, sorry about that. Duh's good, from the pulley comment, right? But I'm getting older now, and how do you think it looks, a guy being poked fun at by his sister, so would you mind it too much going back to Dewey? I'll stop telling on you." He stands at the door, holding the knob, biting his bottom lip. "So?" he says.

I make like I'm thinking. But it's already been decided. I think all my bugging's finally paid off. "Don't stop whining on my account. Do it for yourself, because I'll tell you what makes you look even stupider than I can is you crying on Momma's shoulder for any and every little thing. What do you think those boys on the team would think if they knew that side of you?"

"Yeah, that's cool."

"Then it's settled, Dewey."

He gives me a lopsided smile, cuts the light, then shuts the door, and I'm looking up at the little glow-in-the-dark stars and moon on my ceiling. To see them, I can't look right at them, but sideways. Kind of like how I saw Dewey just now, saw him <u>insignificant</u> and little when looking right at him, and then the next minute all big and bright on a sidewise glance. **4**

There's stars on my ceiling, and I can't stop looking. It's an entire universe up there. ○

4 Interpreting
What causes Missy to look at her brother differently now?

Answering the BIG Question

As you do the following activities, consider the Big Question:
What makes you who you are?

WRITE TO LEARN Think about how Missy's parents treat her. Then write a brief entry in your Learner's Notebook about a time when you felt you were treated unfairly.

PARTNER TALK Meet with a partner who has read "My Self Myself." Discuss the way the parents in this story treat their children and the effect it has on each child.

Vo•cab•u•lary

insignificant (in sig NIF i kant) of little or no importance

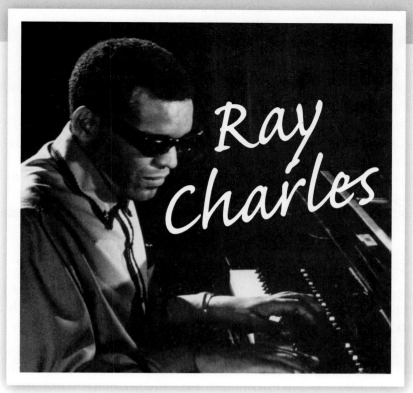

from *The Blues Singers: Ten Who Rocked the World*
by Julius Lester

Read about a legendary musician, who just happened to be blind.

I was born with music inside me. Like my ribs, my liver, my kidneys, my heart.
Like my blood . . . . I release feelings inside me through my songs.
I take some of my sadness, some of the heartache, and turn it out.

— Ray Charles

Born September 23, 1930, Albany, Georgia[1]

His given name is Ray Charles Robinson, but he dropped the Robinson so he wouldn't be confused with the great boxer Sugar Ray Robinson. But you can just call him "The Genius." Everybody will know who you're talking about.

· ·
[1]Ray Charles died in 2004. This article was written when he was still alive.

Ray Charles

Ray grew up in Greenville, Florida, with his mother, Aretha, and his father's first wife, Mary Jane. Some of his earliest memories were of music. A neighbor, Wylie Pitman, owned a café and had a piano. Ray was three years old and was in the café one day when Mr. Pit, as Ray called him, started playing. Ray went over to the piano and "just stared," he recalled. "It <u>astonished</u> and amazed me—his fingers flying, all those chords coming together, the sounds jumping at me and ringing in my ears." From that day on, music was "the only thing I was really anxious to get out of bed for. From the moment I learned that there were piano keys to be mashed, I started mashing 'em, trying to make sounds out of feelings."

When he was five, his four-year-old brother, George, was playing in a tub of water and started struggling. Ray was not strong enough to get him out. By the time Ray ran to the house and brought his mother back, George had drowned.

A few months later Ray started waking up in the mornings to find his eyelids stuck together as if glued. His mother bathed his eyes until they would open, but some minutes would pass before Ray could see clearly. His mother took him to the doctor, who said Ray was going blind and there was nothing anyone could do.

Ray's mother was determined that blindness was not going to prevent him from doing anything he had done before, including his household chores. Once he did a sloppy job of mopping the floor, thinking she would go easy on him because he couldn't see. She made him get on his hands and knees and do the entire floor again.

When Ray was seven, his mother sent him to a school for the deaf and blind in St. Augustine, Florida. During his first year there his right eye began to hurt so badly that it had to be removed. But being blind and losing an eye didn't seem to bother Ray. He quickly learned <u>Braille</u>. Then, because he wanted to communicate with the deaf students, he learned sign language so they could make signs on the palms of his hands while they read his lips.

Vo•cab•u•lary

astonished (uh STAWN isht) greatly surprised
Braille (brayl) a system of raised dots used by the blind to read

Ray's mother died when he was fifteen. He left school and moved to Jacksonville, Florida, where he lived with friends of his "other mother," Mary Jane. The friends offered to buy him a Seeing Eye dog, but he wouldn't even use a cane. Ray said he would "rather stumble a little and maybe bang my knee once or twice—just the way sighted people do." **1**

After a year in Jacksonville he moved to Orlando and then Tampa, where he played with various bands, including a white "hillbilly" group. This was around 1946, a time when it was almost unheard of for a black person to play in a white band, especially one that played country-and-western music. Ray finally decided to leave Florida and asked a friend to look at a map and tell him the name of the city farthest away from Florida. The friend said, "Seattle, Washington." That's where Ray went. He was eighteen.

In Seattle his musical career grew rapidly. Among the musicians he met was a young man named Quincy Jones, who would become a lifelong friend. Quincy became a major force in American music, producing records for Michael Jackson, among others.

Since 1950 Ray Charles's life has been spent making music. He has had many hit records and appeared in the movie *The Blues Brothers* in 1980. In 1986, Ray was one of the original people <u>inducted</u> into the Rock and Roll Hall

> **1 Interpreting**
> Why do you think Ray refused to get a Seeing Eye dog or to use a cane?

Ray Charles, left, accepts his Rock and Roll Hall of Fame award from presenter Quincy Jones.

Vo·cab·u·lary
inducted (in DUK ted) formally admitted

of Fame, along with James Brown and Little Richard [and others]. He received a Grammy Lifetime Achievement Award in 1988.

Ray Charles combined the fervor and spirit of gospel music with the blues and created soul music. But he is <u>versatile</u>, and when he sings songs by the Beatles, country-and-western music, or even something patriotic like "America the Beautiful," he makes familiar songs sound as new as today's sunrise.

Ray Charles is also a remarkable person who has never accepted blindness as a handicap. When he was still a teenager, he learned to drive a car by having whoever was riding with him tell him when he was swerving too far in one direction or the other. He rode motorcycles by listening to the exhaust of the motorcycle in front of him being ridden by a friend. He has been known to pilot planes, is an excellent chess player, fixes his own plumbing, repairs his television and stereo equipment, and types 75 words a minute with no mistakes. ❷

❷ **Responding**
How did you feel about Ray when you found out that he did all of these things, despite being blind?

Ray Charles may be blind. But that doesn't mean he can't see into your soul. ○

Answering the BIG Question

As you do the following activities, consider the Big Question:
What makes you who you are?

WRITE TO LEARN Think about how Ray Charles refused to think of his blindness as a handicap. Where do you think this attitude came from? How did it affect his life? Write down your ideas in a brief entry in your Learner's Notebook.

PARTNER GROUPS With a partner, discuss the Ray Charles quote that appears at the beginning of this selection. What do you think he meant when he said, "I was born with music inside me"? How did music help him deal with his feelings?

Vo·cab·u·lary

versatile (VER suh tul) able to do many activities

Behind the Scenes of... High School Musical

by Gerri Miller

How do you find out who you really are?

Hey, kids, let's put on a show! That's just what the Disney Channel did with the airing of *High School Musical* on January 20, 2006.

It's a musical comedy set in a too-cool high school! With tones of *Grease* and *Romeo and Juliet*, the TV movie focuses on a popular basketball player (Zac Efron) and a brainiac new student (Vanessa Anne Hudgens) who share a love of singing. When they audition for the school musical, sparks fly—romantically for them and socially for the rest of the school.

Scholastic News Online was able to sit down with the stars of *High School Musical*, so check out what one has to say!

ZAC EFRON (Troy Bolton)

SN: We know you from dramas like *Summerland*. Did you have any experience with musicals?

Zac: I began in musical theater. I did *Grease*; I was Harold Hill in *The Music Man*. I had it easier than some guys at the *High School Musical* audition—some of them were passing out! It was Broadway style, seven and a half hours of dancing, singing, and acting. And then we had to play basketball. I was probably weakest at that but I passed—though I didn't find out I got the part for a week and a half.

SN: Sounds grueling!

Zac: Yeah, and then we had two weeks of intense dancing, acting, singing, and basketball rehearsals along with strange stretching [exercises] and things I'd never heard of before. We'd wake up at six in the morning and work until six at night. It was a very long day, but by the end I'd sustained so many injuries and was so sore but so much better than I was before. I learned more in those two weeks than I'd learned in the previous years. Every second of it was worth it. ❶

1 Monitoring Comprehension
Describe the two weeks that Zac spent in rehearsals.

SN: Your character is a superstar athlete

Vo·cab·u·lary

grueling (GROO uh ling) extremely tiring and demanding
sustained (suh STAYND) suffered

who shocks everyone by wanting to star in the musical. Do you relate?

Zac: A little bit, but I was never the cool kid. There's a lot of peer pressure, and you have to take everything you hear with a grain of salt and follow your instincts.

SN: Was it like summer camp for actors, all of you staying in the same hotel?

Zac: Exactly! We became fast friends, and when it was over, everyone was <u>devastated</u>. It was so hard not to be able to go to the hotel room next door and knock. I made a lot of good friends, and we see each other all the time. If I could go back and do it again, I'd do it in a heartbeat.

SN: How do you balance acting and school?

Zac: My priority had always been school first, acting second. Then acting took off and school got put a bit on the back burner, but not too much. I have a really high grade point average. But if I hadn't taken the acting route, I think I might have been <u>valedictorian</u>. I've applied to USC[1] and UCLA[2].

SN: What if both accept you?

Zac: I'll probably go with USC. They have a really good film program.

SN: What will kids learn from watching this movie?

Zac: The message from the movie is that you have to be yourself, walk your own path. Don't listen to all the pressures that come from the outside world. Troy starts off as this hotshot stud, but

. . . .
[1]USC here refers to the University of Southern California.
[2]UCLA is the University of California at Los Angeles.

Vo•cab•u•lary

devastated (DEH vuh stay tud) destroyed or filled with grief
valedictorian (va luh dik TOR ee un) the student who gives the farewell address at graduation, usually the highest-ranked student

he's been given that name by his peers—it's not really who he is. By the end of the movie, he discovers he can be himself and have just as much fun. He goes through this great <u>transformation</u>. By the end of the movie, he's even cooler. ❷

SN: Do you think there will be a sequel to *High School Musical?*

Zac: They're talking about it! ○

> ❷ **Interpreting**
> What makes Troy "even cooler" by the end of the movie?

Answering the BIG Question

As you do the following activities, consider the Big Question:
What makes you who you are?

WRITE TO LEARN According to Zac, the movie's message "is that you have to be yourself, walk your own path." Do you agree with this message? Why or why not? Write down your thoughts in your Learner's Notebook.

LITERATURE GROUPS In a small group, discuss how hard Zac had to work to get the role in *High School Musical* and to rehearse for the movie. Talk about a time when you worked long hours to reach a goal.

Vo•cab•u•lary

transformation (trans fur MAY shun) marked change in nature

241

...and you keep saying I'M the one that plays too many video games!

WRITE TO LEARN If you could be a space alien, what kind would you choose to be? What special powers would you have, and what would be your mission? Describe your alien self in your Learner's Notebook, and write about what you think your choices say about you.

The Whole World in His Hands

by Hope Anita Smith

When you look at pictures of your family, what do you think?

I am looking at a photograph of
my family.
We are all smiling—
like someone has just told us
a good joke.
My momma sits stately
in a <u>regal</u>-looking chair.

Vo•cab•u•lary
regal (REE gul) suitable for royalty

My grandmomma stands
behind her because she's
"not that old."
My brother and sister are seated
at Momma's feet.
I am standing next to Grandmomma,
my hands laced together in front of me
in plain view,
because Grandmomma doesn't want
anyone to think that I am there
to hold her up.

And then there is my daddy.
He stands behind us
towering over us all.
One hand rests on my shoulder,
We are his world. ❶
And he's got the whole world
in his hands. ○

❶ **Interpreting**
Why can the father rest his hand on his daughter's shoulder, while the daughter cannot have her hand on or even near her grandmother?

**Answering the
BIG Question**

As you do the following activities, consider the Big Question:
What makes you who you are?

WRITE TO LEARN Think about the idea of a family photograph. Write a brief entry in your Learner's Notebook reflecting on what a person can understand about himself or herself by looking at a family photograph.

LITERATURE GROUPS Meet with two or three others who have read "The Whole World in His Hands." Discuss the reasons people are concerned about how they look to others.

Epiphany

by Ellen Wittlinger

Social forces like racism can make a person closed-minded and unable to trust others.

On the first day of first grade, Epiphany[1] Jones became my best friend. She had just moved to Bristol that summer and didn't know anybody yet, which was lucky for me. That was our first year of sitting at desks, and we had one of those alphabetizing teachers, so I, DeMaris Kanakis, sat right behind Epiphany Jones.

. . . .

[1]Epiphany's name is a word that refers to a moment of sudden, great understanding of truth.

Epiphany

I could hardly believe there was actually a girl like Epiphany in my school. In kindergarten I had to hang out with the boys—who sometimes acted dumb as doorknobs, but at least enjoyed a good argument—because the girls in my class were just too girly. At recess they'd cluster around the teacher and try to hold her hand. I couldn't figure out what was wrong with them. They never seemed to have an idea more exciting than trading lunch box sandwiches.

But Epiphany and I were on the same page. For six years we made Kimball Elementary School a fun place to be—at least it was fun for us. We did everything bigger and longer and louder than anybody else, boys included. We built gigantic science projects that almost worked; we sang higher than anybody else in the chorus; we talked so much we had to be de-alphabetized; we bloodied our noses and broke our bones (once I broke one of Jack Glover's, too); and our favorite teacher (Mrs. Tolliver, fourth grade) said it broke her heart to see us move on to fifth. Kimball was a small school, so teachers from the next year would see us in the hallway and say, "DeMaris and Epiphany! I'm waiting for you!" We'd just laugh.

For our sixth-grade graduation, Epiphany and I got matching dresses. Even our mothers didn't know about it—it was a well-planned scheme. The dresses were bright blue, so you could see them quite well even from the back of the auditorium where our parents were sitting. When I won the Attendance Award, Epiphany stood up with me, and when she won the Best Speller Award, I stood up with her, arm in arm, as if we were locked together. Even though the prissy girls rolled their eyes, plenty of people thought we were funny. That's all it took to keep us going.

Unfortunately, Epiphany's parents did *not* think we were funny. They weren't too crazy about me, or Kimball Elementary, or the whole town of Bristol, I guess. They'd moved here for her dad's job, but as soon as school got out her parents would pack Epiphany and her brother off to spend the summer in Tennessee with their aunt and uncle and cousins. Epiphany didn't mind, because there were lots of kids to play with there, and I guess they were almost as much fun as I was. But I hated the summers when she was gone; they were long and boring. I killed time by becoming the cartwheel champion of Bristol and never walked anywhere I could cartwheel instead. It was something to do while I waited for Epiphany to come back.

Two days before the start of seventh grade, Epiphany returned from Tennessee and called me up.

"Hey," she said, "I'm back."

"Thank the Lord," I said. "Come over here right now. We have to figure things out!"

"Whataya mean, 'figure things out?'" she said. This was my first clue that something was wrong, but I tried to ignore it. Epiphany *always* knew what I meant without having to ask. We had practically the same brain.

"You know," I said. "Like, what to wear on the first day, and what kind of book bag to bring—this is junior high, you know. And bring your schedule over so we can see what classes we have together and which teachers."

She gave a big sigh as if I'd asked her to do something hard. "Okay, but I'll have to come tomorrow."

"Tomorrow hardly gives us any time!" I protested. "We need to make plans!"

"DeMaris, I don't intend to start junior high school wearing the same exact outfit as you, you know. We're not children anymore."

For a minute I didn't know what to say, which hardly ever happens. "I know we aren't. I'm not saying dress *identically*. I'm just saying, talk about it."

"I already know what I'm wearing," Epiphany said. "My cousin and I talked about it this summer. But if you want me to come over tomorrow to help you, I will."

It was the beginning of things going crooked between us. ❶

Still, being at the junior high was exciting enough for me to overlook it for a while. There are six elementary schools in Bristol that all go to the junior high, so every class was full of strange faces. I even loved the hallways—no more little kids bumping

❶ **Monitoring Comprehension**
What has changed between Epiphany and DeMaris?

into you or crying or yelling. Here people leaned against their lockers and had low, important conversations with each other, like grown-ups. Some of the teachers even called us "Miss" or "Mister," which cracked me up every time.

The downside was that Epiphany and I had no classes together. After the first few days of newness wore off, I missed her terribly. When a teacher said something really dumb, there was nobody to look at and make faces with. Of course, we'd meet in the cafeteria for lunch and make jokes about the awful food before we built towers out of the mashed potatoes and stuck little corn windows all over them or made a house out of mystery meat and <u>thatched</u> the roof with coleslaw.

I started noticing, though, that Epiphany's heart wasn't really in it. Sometimes I'd catch her staring over at this big round table in the corner of the cafeteria where all the black kids usually ate. There were more black kids at the junior high than one table's worth, but not too many more, and the extra people just pulled chairs from other tables and squeezed in tight. ❷

❷ **Interpreting**
Why do you think Epiphany's attitude toward DeMaris is changing?

One day I asked Epiphany, "Do you wish you could eat with them instead of me?" I only asked this because I was absolutely sure that she'd laugh at me and say, "Are you crazy?" But she didn't. She stuck two fingers in her potato pile and said quietly, "Sometimes."

If you haven't figured it out yet, Epiphany is black and I am white. It never seemed to matter to her when we were at Kimball, where she was the only black kid, but at the junior high there were others, and it seemed like there was some kind of gravity pulling her over to them.

So I decided to be cool about it. "Well," I said. "You could eat with them sometimes."

Vo•cab•u•lary
thatched (thacht) covered

"Who would you eat with?" Epiphany asked me.

"I don't know," I said, looking around the big room. "Maybe her." I pointed to a girl I recognized from my English class who was sitting alone at a table, reading a book.

Epiphany nodded. "Well, maybe someday I will then. Thanks." She looked at me sideways, sort of embarrassed, a look I'd never ever seen on her before. My stomach was balled up like I'd just eaten glue, but I smiled back at her, hoping "someday" would never come.

But it did. All that year Epiphany went back and forth between my table and the big table where the black kids ate. I got to know the girl who read books. Her name was Holly Lembach and she was more fun than she looked like at first, but she did not have the same brain I did, and she often didn't know what I meant, and most of the time we were not on the same page.

I felt sad the whole year. Even my mother noticed that I wasn't my usual cheery self. "Have you had an argument with Epiphany?" she asked. "She doesn't come over as much as she used to."

When I said we hadn't, Mom said, "Sometimes friendships change when you get older. You make new friends."

Epiphany

It was just some of that usual mother talk to make you feel better, but I wasn't in the mood for it. "I don't want to make any new friends!" I yelled at her, then slammed the door to my room so the discussion could not continue.

The summer before eighth grade, Epiphany went down to Tennessee again. In a funny way I didn't mind so much. I mean if she was in Tennessee, just like every other summer, I could make myself believe nothing had changed—that we were still best friends. It was when she was here in Bristol, sitting across the cafeteria from me, that I wasn't so sure.

Holly and I were hanging around together a lot by then. She liked having sleepovers where we read magazines and tried out new hairstyles on each other. It was kind of girly, but I actually didn't mind as much as I thought I would. Holly turned thirteen two weeks before I did. To celebrate, her parents took us to a theater in Boston to see *Rent*, and then we went out for dinner to an expensive restaurant and ordered salmon. We both wore makeup and high heels. It was the most grown-up kind of celebration I'd ever been to, and I started thinking maybe Holly was just as much fun as Epiphany. ❸

> **❸ Interpreting**
> What is changing about DeMaris and her life?

Still, a few days before school started, I called the Joneses' house.

"Oh, DeMaris," Mrs. Jones said, sounding a little <u>aggravated</u>, as usual. "Epiphany isn't home now."

"But she's back from Tennessee?" I said.

Her mother paused, then said simply, "Yes, she is."

I asked her to have Epiphany call me when she got back, but I never got a call. It made me mad that her mother didn't give Epiphany my message. What did I ever do to her?

I didn't see her until the first day of school, in the cafeteria. Holly and I were already in line when Epiphany came in with a

Vo•cab•u•lary
aggravated (AG ruh vay ted) annoyed

group of black kids. I waved at her.

"Save my place," I told Holly, and ran over to hug Epiphany. But when I got close and saw the look on her face, I knew a hug would not be appreciated. Over the summer her looks had changed. Her wild hair, which she'd always tied back with scarves or up with ribbons, was cropped to half an inch all around her head.

"Hey," she said, without smiling.

"Hey," I said, feeling Epiphany's new friends' eyes on me. "I called you. Didn't you get my message?"

She studied her elbow. "I got it."

"Oh." How could we have a conversation under such <u>scrutiny</u>? "Holly is saving my place at the front of the line. Do you want to eat with us?"

As soon as I asked the question, I knew the answer. One of the tall black boys <u>snickered</u>.

"I don't think so," Epiphany said. "I'll see you around, though."

"Okay," I said, and watched her turn away, her new pack of friends surrounding her like she was a magnet and they were nails. I was so angry I felt like crying, but instead I <u>ranted</u> to Holly. ❹

"Epiphany is such a snob now! She acts like we were never even friends! She has to do everything with *those* kids."

Holly shrugged. "That's just how it is. They stick together. We stick together."

"But *why?*" I really wanted to know, but Holly was no expert.

❹ **Interpreting**
Why does Epiphany treat DeMaris so coldly?

Vo•cab•u•lary

scrutiny (SKROO tuh nee) close examination
snickered (SNIH kurd) laughed in a mean way
ranted (RANT ud) talked in an excited manner

"That's just how it *is*," she repeated. "I like Epiphany too, but I don't think she'll be eating lunch with us anymore." **5**

"Well, that's just stupid," I said. "Just plain stupid."

Holly gave me half of her lemon square to cheer me up.

For weeks I ate my lunch with one eye on the black kids' table. Everybody was crazy about Epiphany, you could tell. Which made me remember why I liked her too. She could crack you up with a sideways look and then keep you laughing until you were too weak to breathe. When Epiphany was your friend, you felt special, even if everybody else thought you were weird. I couldn't believe she wasn't my friend anymore—it didn't make any sense.

"DeMaris, are you listening to me?" Holly said one day.

I focused my attention on her. "What? Sorry."

"I said I can't go to the movies with you on Saturday night this week."

"How come?" We'd gotten into a habit of going every weekend, unless the movies were really bad.

She smiled oddly. "This guy asked me to go to the dance."

"What dance?" I asked. "What guy?"

"There's a dance here, at school, on Saturday night. I swear, you don't pay attention to anything anymore, except *that table*. A guy in my algebra class asked me to go. Rick Saloman."

"Oh." I was caught off guard. A guy? Somehow it hadn't occurred to me that Holly was thinking about guys. But I guess most girls were. Even I had to admit that some of my old kindergarten friends had grown into good-looking guys. I just didn't have a clue what to do about it.

Holly pointed Rick Saloman out to me. He was sitting at a table full of boys, one of whom was pretending to choke so he could spit out his soda dramatically and make a big mess. Not Rick, though. He looked decent. When he saw us looking, he waved.

5 Responding
How do you feel about what has happened between DeMaris and Epiphany?

By the next Monday we had a new addition to our lunch table. Rick and Holly sat next to each other, rubbing shoulders and sharing french fries. They talked about the dance they'd gone to on Saturday, and the movie they saw together on Sunday afternoon—the movie I *hadn't* seen. I ate my own french fries and tried not to look at them.

Rick had class in the other direction from Holly and me, so when I got her alone, I said, "Is he always going to eat with us now?"

"He's my boyfriend, DeMaris, I *have* to eat lunch with him!"

"Already he's your boyfriend? That was fast."

"Listen," she said. "Having lunch with you is like eating alone anyway. All you do is stare at Epiphany. Why don't you just go over there and eat with them!"

It was an idea that had never occurred to me. Just go over and eat with them. Could I do that? "Maybe I will!" I told Holly. "Then you and your boyfriend can grin at each other like idiots without an audience."

She stalked away.

I started getting nervous by third period on Tuesday. Should I ask permission to sit there or just plunk my tray down like I belonged? I'd have to get there early enough to get a seat by

Epiphany, but not too early in case I didn't know the other kids at the table. By the time I got myself through the lunch line (and noticed Holly and Rick already seated at a table for two), I'd decided not to think about it anymore—to just do it.

I waited until I saw Epiphany sit down next to a girl from my gym class named Lena, then I hurried over and pulled up a chair on her other side, slapped my tray on the table, and smiled.

"Hi, Lena. Hi, Epiphany." I took a bite of burger and looked past my onetime best friend to speak to Lena. "Do you think we'll have to do rope climbing in gym again today? My hands are still sore from yesterday. You got even farther up than I did."

Both of them were staring at me, Epiphany with narrowed eyes.

Finally Lena spoke. "Um, yeah, my hands hurt too."

By then a group of boys had joined the table. It was getting full and kids were pulling up chairs to crowd in. Every new person who arrived stared at me, but nobody said a word. The only other person at the table whose name I knew was this guy Theon from my history class, so I smiled at him, too. "Hi, Theon! How're you?"

Silence. Big, awful silence. Man, it was like wearing a Yankees hat in Fenway Park. I felt like I'd walked into a funeral parlor where everybody knew the dead guy but me. People chugged their lunches and left, some of them glaring at me like I was the <u>plague</u>, most ignoring me completely. When Epiphany was done, she stood up and looked down at me. **6**

"I need to talk to you, DeMaris."

"Okay." We dumped our trays and headed for the door. Epiphany didn't say anything until we were outside the building and around the corner, out of sight of almost everybody.

"What do you think you're doing?" she asked

6 Visualizing
Can you picture what happens after DeMaris sits down at Epiphany's lunch table?

Vo•cab•u•lary

plague (playg) a contagious disease

me, straight out. She was madder than I'd ever seen her, but I stayed calm.

"Eating lunch with you," I said.

"Well, you can't eat at that table."

"Why not? It's a free country."

"That's what you think." Epiphany put her hands on her hips and surveyed me as though I were a new species instead of an old friend. "What happened to Holly? I thought you ate with her."

"She's got a boyfriend. They want to be alone."

Epiphany rolled her eyes—she is the best eye roller I know. "Well, I'm sorry, DeMaris, but you cannot eat at our table!"

"Why?"

"Because it makes everybody uncomfortable. Can't you tell that?"

"Yes. But I still don't know why. We were best friends for six years. How come all of a sudden you can't even sit at a lunch table with me?" Just saying it out loud made the sadness bunch up at the back of my throat, making my voice sound thick.

Epiphany leaned in close, as though she was going to tell me a secret. She laid her arm next to mine. "Because you are white, DeMaris, and I am black. Very simple."

I pulled my arm away. "Oh. And when we were in first grade and third grade and sixth grade, you weren't black then? I wasn't white then?"

"How can I make you get it?" she said, sighing. "Black kids need to stick together when we get older. You can't understand us. We're just too different now."

"We've still got two legs, two arms, two eyes, and big mouths—just like we always did."

She stamped her foot. "You aren't even trying to understand. DeMaris, do you see how many black kids there are at this school?"

"Yeah, pretty many."

"Pretty many? You think a dozen is pretty many?"

"Well, that's more than there were at Kimball."

"Which is why my parents hated Kimball so much."

"But you didn't hate it. We had fun there! I'm not saying you shouldn't have black friends too, but how come, all of a sudden, I don't even exist?"

"Because things change!" Her voice got kind of quiet. "We're not little kids anymore, DeMaris. We live in a bigger world now. I'm not saying it's your fault—that's just how it is between black people and white people. You just have to accept it." Her mouth curled down at one corner in a sad smile, and then she turned and walked away.

Of course, Epiphany should have known—I'm not the "accepting" kind.

On Wednesday I got to the table before she did. Theon and a couple of other boys were there, and one other girl I didn't know. I smacked my tray down, but kept standing.

I looked at Theon. "Why is it such a big deal if I want to eat here?"

Every one of them stared at me until I was starting to feel like you do in those dreams where you're up on stage and suddenly you realize you're naked. Finally Theon leaned way back in his chair and said, "'Cause you can eat at any table you want to."

I took a deep breath. "No I can't," I said. "I don't know most of these kids, and the ones I do know, I don't like very much."

A girl laughed, but it wasn't a nice laugh. "You don't know us, either. How come you think you like us so much?"

"She's one a them wanna-bes," another boy said. "We so cool, she thinks our cool blackness gonna rub off on her, she start getting darker and darker."

Just as they were all laughing at that <u>hysterical</u> idea, Epiphany showed up.

I pointed to her and watched her eyes get huge and round. "She's the reason I want to sit here. I know her as well as I know myself—she was my best friend for six years. Why do I have to give her up now just because I'm not black?" ❼

Epiphany turned around and walked away. She dumped her whole tray of crappy food in the trash and marched right out of the cafeteria.

> **❼ Responding**
> Do you think it took courage to do what DeMaris is doing here? Why or why not?

"Now that was just plain wasteful," Theon said. There was a low <u>murmur</u> of laughter, but most of the kids just stared at their plates. Lena had been standing behind Epiphany, watching the whole thing. She dropped her tray on the table and said, "You gonna eat standing up, girl?"

"Can . . . can I sit here?"

"You just told us you could, didn't you?"

So I sat. After a minute, the kids started talking to each other. Nobody said anything else to me, but at least they weren't all silent like the day before. And they weren't talking about anything especially *black*, as far as I could tell. I understood every single thing they said.

Vo•cab•u•lary

hysterical (his TAIR ih kul) extremely funny
murmur (MUR mur) a low sound

Epiphany

On Thursday Epiphany was waiting for me at the bottom of the cafeteria stairs. "Are you planning on ruining my life again today?" she said.

"Are you planning on throwing your lunch away and making a big scene?"

"Why are you doing this to me?" she wailed.

She sounded so upset, it made me feel terrible too. "I'm not doing it to hurt you, Epiphany! I just *miss* you!"

She turned away and looked up the stairs for a long time. Then she said, "Oh, what the —. Come on."

By the time we got to the table everybody else was there and we had to squeeze in on either side of Theon. He and another boy were arguing about something.

"You think that Richards guy gonna give you a part, man? You wasting your time, Stokes. He doing Shakespeare, brother. He don't want no black Romeos."

A couple of kids looked over at us as we sat down, but the conversation continued.

"It's not *Romeo and Juliet* anyway," the boy called Stokes said. "It's *A Midsummer Night's Dream*. It's cool. I saw it last summer with my parents."

"I've seen it," Lena said. "You could be the guy who gets turned into a jackass."

"Oh, that is definitely the part that Richards guy will like you for, Stokes, man." Theon put his head back and laughed like one himself.

"I'm going to the play auditions too," I said. "At three o'clock, right?"

The conversation came to a crashing halt. Suddenly turkey burgers were being devoured.

Then Stokes said, "Yeah, three o'clock."

I nodded. "Anybody else going? Epiphany, you should try out.

You'd be great."

Another silence. But then Theon spoke up. "What's your name again, girl? Something weird, I know."

"DeMaris," I said. "DeMaris Kanakis."

"That's a mouthful," Lena said.

Theon continued. "DeMaris Kanakis, maybe you don't know it, but Mr. Richards, the drama teacher, don't like black people. He wouldn't put one a us in his old play if his hair was on fire and we had the hose." **8**

"Why do you think that?" I asked.

"'Why do you think that?'" Theon repeated in a high, silly voice.

"He thinks that," Epiphany said, "because when Theon took the drama class last year, Mr. Richards wouldn't let him use street talk when he was doing scenes like: *To be or not to be: dat bees da question.*"

Lena chuckled, but Theon looked furious. "You disrespecting me in front of this white girl, Epiphany?"

"Just saying what I know." She sucked her milk through the straw.

Theon glared at me. "You know what that Richards guy said to me? He said, 'Theon, you talk like a criminal!' That's what he said! *'Theon, you talk like a criminal!'* Who he think he is, saying something like that? I ain't no criminal."

The table of people murmured agreement.

"I know," Stokes said, "T.J. had a bad story about him too—he's not cool, but I want to try out anyway. I want to show that guy I can act!"

"Anyway, Theon," I said. "Mr. Richards

> **8 Monitoring Comprehension**
> According to Theon, why won't any of the black kids get a part in the play?

probably didn't know you can speak as well as anybody else when you want to."

Theon's eyes got big as Epiphany leaped out of her chair, grabbing my arm with one hand. "Let's go, DeMaris. I knew something like this would happen. You just don't *get* it!"

She was still explaining to me what it was I didn't get after school, when we went to play auditions. She was still sort of mad, but I was so glad she was trying out for the play with me, I didn't mind too much.

"What you don't understand, DeMaris, is that talking like that *is* talking well, as far as Theon is concerned. As far as a lot of us are concerned. It's *our* language, just for us."

"You don't talk that way."

"Not in front of you. But I do sometimes, when I want to."

"But it makes white people think you want to be different," I said.

"We're treated different anyhow—we might as well <u>flaunt</u> it. Be proud of it!" **9**

"You weren't different from me before," I said, but Epiphany wasn't listening. She was determined to teach me a few things, then and there.

"You can't say stuff like that to Theon—or anybody who's black—because *you're not.* And don't try to explain other white people to us, like we're too stupid to understand. If you're gonna come and eat with us, shut up and listen for a while, until you start to get how it is. Otherwise nobody is gonna say

9 Monitoring Comprehension
What is Epiphany trying to make DeMaris understand about the language that African Americans sometimes use?

Vo·cab·u·lary

flaunt (flawnt) to show to others in a big way

one word in front of you."

"But I didn't say Theon was stupid. I said just the opposite!"

"You think you did, DeMaris, but believe me, that's not how it sounded to us."

I sighed. "Is it always going to be like this now? You're part of an *us* and I'm not?"

She shrugged and sighed, but then her mouth turned up a little bit at the corner. "You're sitting at the table, aren't you?"

The auditions lasted almost three hours—there were at least sixty kids trying out, and Mr. Richards had us each read several parts. Epiphany and I got better and better every time we had to read; I knew bigmouthed crazy girls like us would be great actors. Stokes was there too; I watched Mr. Richards's face when Stokes read parts to see if I could catch him being prejudiced, but I decided it might not show right out front where I could see it. I did notice that he never looked directly *at* Stokes, the way he did the other boys. I bet Stokes noticed too. I knew Theon would have.

That night, for the first time in almost six months, Epiphany called me on the phone, and we laughed about all the stuff that had happened at the auditions. I was so happy I could hardly sleep.

Friday morning I ran to school. Mr. Richards had told us the callback list would be posted outside the theater door. If your name was on the list you were pretty sure to get a part, but you'd have to stay after school again for more auditions. I could see Epiphany standing at the board as I ran down the hallway.

"Did we make it?"

She whirled around and gave me a hug. "Of course we did! We are the best!"

After we danced around a minute, I looked at the list, just to see my name for myself. "Look! Stokes made it too! What do you think Theon will say now?"

Epiphany's smile folded into a grim line. "I don't know, but whatever he says, don't you say anything back! You hear me?"

"I know, I know—just listen."

And, boy, did I listen. Theon was going on about how Mr. Richards was gonna make fools out of Stokes and Epiphany, how he'd never give them decent parts because he was a racist. Then Epiphany said that, well, maybe he *was* a racist, she didn't know, but he was also the director of the play, so she expected he'd give the best parts to the best people. And then Lena said if he was a racist he might not be able to see who was best because he'd be blinded by his own prejudices, and then Theon said why would black people even want to be in a play with a racist directing it, and then Stokes said because the world was full of racists and you couldn't just hide from them—you had to show them they were wrong, and then Theon called Stokes an idiot. I just sat and listened and hoped Epiphany was proud of me. ❿

❿ Monitoring Comprehension
What is the difference between Theon's view of how a person should deal with racism and Stokes's view?

Once we got on stage again that afternoon, I just knew we were going to get good parts. A lot of the other girls seemed scared to death they'd make a mistake. Their voices were too small, they stood in one spot like they were nailed to the floor, and they looked ready to bust out crying half the time. Epiphany and I were just having fun, the way we always did.

Over the weekend we talked on the phone twice; once she called me and once I called her. We made plans to meet at the drama board first thing Monday morning to see what parts we'd gotten. We kept squealing to each other until her mother told her to stop making that awful noise. Her mother would probably have made an awful noise too, if she'd known who her daughter was talking to.

When Epiphany and I walked up to the lunch table Monday, we held our heads up like queens. Epiphany actually *was* a queen: Titania, queen of the fairies! And I got the part of Helena, one of the mixed-up lovers. Both of these are really good parts, and we were jumpy with excitement. Lena congratulated us first, and everybody else did too, except Theon, who just shook his head like we were all crazy. But we weren't the real stars. Turns out Stokes got the part of Puck, which is the biggest and best role of all. Puck is this mischievous forest <u>imp</u> who gets to leap all over the stage and play tricks on people. Stokes was so amazed, he couldn't believe it.

"So, what do you think now, Theon?" he said.

Theon snorted. "Doesn't prove anything. I still say, you better not turn your back on Richards. He's white, and don't you forget it."

Lena and Stokes glanced at me sideways. Epiphany frowned into her sandwich. I knew she didn't want me to say anything but there are times you just can't keep your mouth shut.

"*I'm* white," I said.

Theon let his mouth drop open. "No kidding?"

Epiphany poked me with her sneaker, but I moved my foot away. "So, does that automatically mean you don't trust me?"

Theon squirmed a little in his chair, but he looked me right in the eye. "If you're white and I don't know you, I don't trust you."

I nodded. "Okay, but if you got to know me, you might trust me?"

"And how would I be gettin' to know you?"

"Maybe we could eat lunch at the same table," I said, smiling. Stokes <u>stifled</u> a laugh.

Theon rolled his eyes; he's almost as good at it as Epiphany. "You," he said, pointing at me and shaking his head. "You. I don't know. I don't know."

"Like, is there a 10 percent chance, you think, or more than that?" I said.

Theon looked like he was trying hard not to laugh, but Lena let out a hoot.

"DeMaris Kanakis, I like the way you say things straight out," she told me.

Vo·cab·u·lary

imp (imp) a small, magical creature
stifled (STY fuld) smothered; held back

I smiled. "So, it's not such a terrible thing that I came to sit at your table, huh?"

Theon let his head fall into his hand and actually smiled. Epiphany wrapped her leg around mine and said, "I knew you were crazy from the first minute I saw you, DeMaris. The very first minute."

A few weeks later, Holly dumped Rick Saloman. She pulled me aside in the lunch line. "Do you think they'd let me eat at the black table too?" she asked me.

"I think it's the black-and-white table now," I said.

When she sat down I introduced her to Lena and Stokes and some of the other kids. They mostly said, "Hey," like it was no big deal.

Then Theon said, "Holly? What kinda name's that supposed to be? Like a holly *bush*? Huh! I wouldn't stand for my mother naming me after no bush."

Holly stared Theon in the eyes. "I like my name. It's very . . . green."

Theon's eyes got big. "Oh, no, this one thinks she's *green*! We turnin' into a doggone rainbow coalition!"

"Stranger things have happened," Epiphany and I said simultaneously, then squealed with laughter.

We were back. **11** ○

11 Interpreting
How have the characters in the story managed to move beyond the barriers of racism?

Answering the BIG Question

As you do the following activities, consider the Big Question:
What makes you who you are?

WRITE TO LEARN Think about racist attitudes in our society. Write a brief entry in your Learner's Notebook about ways that ordinary people can challenge such attitudes.

PARTNER TALK Pair with a partner who has read "Epiphany." Discuss why Ellen Wittlinger wrote this story. Do you think she achieved her purpose? Why or why not?

Mama's Magic

by Glenis Redmond

A mama has the power to make her child feel a sense of confidence.

My Mama is Magic!
Always was and always will be.
There is one phrase that <u>constantly</u> bubbled
from the lips of her five children, "My mama can do it."
We thought mama knew everything.
Believed she did, as if she were born full grown from the
Encyclopedia Britannica.
I could tell you stories.
How she <u>transformed</u> a run down paint
peeled shack into a home.
How she heated us with tin tub baths from
a kettle on a stove.
Poured it over in there like an <u>elixir</u>. ❶

> ❶ **Visualizing**
> Create pictures in your mind as you read this poem.

Vo•cab•u•lary

constantly (KON stunt lee) again and again
transformed (trans FORMD) changed into something new
elixir (ih LIK sur) magical potion

Mama's Magic

We were my mama's favorite recipe.
She whipped us up from a big brown bowl,
supported by her big brown arms.

We were homemade children.
Stitched together with homemade love.
We didn't get everything we wanted
but lacked for nothing.

My mama was protection!
Like those quilts her mother used to make.
She tucked us in with patches of cut out history all around us.
We found we could walk anywhere in this world and not feel alone.

My mama never whispered the shame of poverty in our ears.
She taught us to dance to our own shadows.
Pay no attention to those grand parties on
the other side of the track.
Make your own music she'd say
as she walked, as she cleaned
the sagging floorboards of that place.
You'll get there, You'll get there.
Her broom seemed to say with every wisp.
We looked at the stars in my mama's eyes,
they told us we owned the world.
We walked like kings and queens even on midnight trips to
the outhouse.
We were under her spell. My mama didn't study at no
Harvard or Yale but the things she knew
you couldn't learn from no book!
Like . . .
how to make your life sing like sweet potato pie sweetness
out of an open window.
How to make anybody feel at home.
How at just the right moment be silent,
be silent, then with her eyes say, "everything gonna be alright,
child,
everything is gonna be alright."

How she tended to our sickness.
How she raised our spirits.
How she kept flowers living
on our <u>dilapidated</u> porch
in the <u>midst</u> of family <u>chaos</u>.
My mama raised children like it was her business in life.
Put us on her hip and kept moving.
Keeping that house Pine-sol clean.
Yeah, my mama is magic.
Always was and always will be.
Her magic. How to stay steady and sure in this fast pace world.
Now when people look at me
with my head held high.
My back erect and say,
Who does she think she is?
I just keep walking
with the <u>assurance</u> inside. **2**
I am Black Magic.
And I am Jeanette Redmond's child. ○

> **2 Interpreting**
> Where does the speaker's confidence seem to come from?

Answering the BIG Question

As you do the following activities, consider the Big Question:
What makes you who you are?

WRITE TO LEARN Think about the effect the speaker's mama had on her. Who has influenced you the most? Write about this person in your Learner's Notebook.

LITERATURE GROUPS Meet with two or three others who have read "Mama's Magic." Discuss what you think it takes to teach children to believe in themselves.

Vo·cab·u·lary

dilapidated (dih LAP ih day tid) broken down
midst (midst) middle
chaos (KAY os) disorder and confusion
assurance (uh SHUR uns) confidence

Index of Authors and Titles

Acknowledgments

Literature credits

Unit 1

From "Star Spotlight" by Gerri Miller. Published in *Scholastic News*, February 28, 2006. Copyright © 2006 by Scholastic Inc. Reprinted by permission.

From *Travel Team* by Mike Lupica, copyright © 2004 by Mike Lupica. Used by permission of Philomel Books, A Division of Penguin Young Readers Group, a Member of Penguin Group (USA) Inc., 345 Hudson Street, New York NY. All rights reserved.

"Silent Dance: Dancing with the Deaf" by Nancy Bo Flood. From *Appleseeds'* May 2004 issue: *Becoming a Dancer*, © 2004 Carus Publishing Company, published by Cobblestone Publishing, 30 Grove St., Suite C, Peterborough, NH 03458. All rights reserved. Used by permission of the publisher.

"Dancers on Wheels" by Janeen R. Adil, from *Appleseeds'* May 2004 issue: *Becoming a Dancer*, © 2004 Carus Publishing Company, published by Cobblestone Publishing, 30 Grove St., Suite C, Peterborough, NH 03458. All rights reserved. Used by permission of the publisher.

"Mario and His Fields of Dreams" reprinted with the permission of Simon & Schuster Books for Young Readers, an imprint of Simon & Schuster Children's Publishing Division from *The Macmillan Book of Baseball Stories* by Terry Egan, Stan Friedmann and Mike Levine. Copyright © 1992 by Terry Egan, Stan Friedmann and Mike Levine.

"Kids Voting USA" by Katherine House, from *Appleseeds'* September 2004 issue: *Vote!* © 2004 Carus Publishing Company, published by Cobblestone Publishing, 30 Grove St., Suite C, Peterborough, NH 03458. All rights reserved. Used by permission of the publisher.

"Word Wise" by Bizet Kizcorn.

"The Dare" from *Danitra Brown Leaves Town* by Nikki Grimes. Copyright © 2002 by Nikki Grimes. Used by permission of HarperCollins Publishers.

"Who Turned on the Faucet?" by Sarah E. Romanov. Reprinted by permission of *Spider* magazine, September 2005, Vol. 12, No. 9, text copyright © 2005 by Sarah E. Romanov.

"The Red Lion" by Diane Wolkstein, from *More Best-Loved Stories Told at the National Storytelling Festival*. Copyright © 1992 by the National Association for the Preservation and Perpetuation of Storytelling. Reprinted by permission of the National Storytelling Network.

From *What Do You Care What Other People Think?: Further Adventures of a Curious Character* by Richard P. Feynman as told to Ralph Leighton. Copyright © 1988 by Gweneth Feynman and Ralph Leighton. Used by permission of W. W. Norton & Company, Inc.

"Abuelito Who" from *My Wicked Wicked Ways*. Copyright © 1987 by Sandra Cisneros. Published by Third Woman Press and in hardcover by Alfred A. Knopf. Reprinted by permission of Susan Bergholz Literary Services, New York. All rights reserved.

"Macona, the Honest Warrior" by Barbara Winther, from *Plays from Hispanic Tales* reprinted with the permission of the publisher Plays/ Sterling Partners, Inc. Copyright © 1998 Plays, PO Box 600160, Newton, MA 02460.

Unit 2

"The Blue Darter" by Judith Logan Lehne. *Highlights for Children*, June 1992. Copyright © 1992 by Highlights for Children, Inc., Columbus, OH. Reprinted by permission.

"Scout's Honor" by Avi. Copyright © 1996 by Avi. Originally appeared in *When I Was Your Age: Original Stories About Growing Up.* Reprinted by permission of Brandt & Hochman Literary Agents, Inc.

From "Tracy McGrady" by Denise Henry. Published in *Scholastic Action,* October 24, 2005. Copyright © 2005 by Scholastic Inc. Reprinted by permission.

"The Calamity Kids in Weakness of Will!" by Jerzy Drozd and Sara Turner.

"Inside Scoop: Racing Stripes" from *National Geographic Kids,* December 2005. Reprinted by permission of the National Geographic Society.

"Experts, Incorporated" by Sarah Weeks. Reprinted by permission of Pippin Properties, Inc.

"Why music matters: program helps students learn to tune in to life" by Kari Ridge. *Know Your World Extra,* September 26, 2003. Copyright © 2003 Weekly Reader Corporation. Reprinted by permission.

"A Cowboy's Diary" by Walter Dean Myers from *Scholastic Storyworks,* February/March 1999. Adapted from *My Name is America, the Journal of Joshua Loper, a Black Cowboy* by Walter Dean Myers. Copyright © 1999 by Walter Dean Myers. Reprinted by permission of Scholastic Inc.

"I Jump Field" by Christa Champion. Reprinted by permission of the author.

"On Stage" from *Out of the Dust* by Karen Hesse. Published by Scholastic Press/ Scholastic Inc. Copyright © 1997 by Karen Hesse. Reprinted by permission.

"Breaking Down the Walls" by Kathryn D. Sullivan. *Highlights for Children,* December 2004. Copyright © 2004 by Highlights for Children, Inc., Columbus, Ohio. Reprinted by permission.

Excerpt from *Frida Kahlo: Portrait of a Mexican Painter* by Bárbara C. Cruz. Copyright © 1996 by Bárbara C. Cruz. Reprinted by permission of Enslow Publishers, Inc.

"Rock Takes a Name" by Tim Myers. Reprinted by permission of the author.

Unit 3

"The Elian Gonzalez Story" by Michael Dahlie, from *Scholastic Read-Aloud Anthology,* by Janet Allen and Patrick Daley. Published by Scholastic Teaching Resources/Scholastic Inc. Copyright © 2004 by Janet Allen and Patrick Daley. Reprinted by permission.

"Falling Off the Empire State Building" by Harry Mazer. Reprinted by permission of Sterling Lord Literistic.

"Elizabeth Eckford" from *We Were There, Too!* by Phillip Hoose. Copyright © 2001 by Phillip Hoose. Reprinted by permission of Farrar Straus & Giroux LLC.

"The Water Pot and the Necklace" from *The Cow of No Color* by Nina Jaffe and Steve Zeitlin. Copyright © 1998 by Nina Jaffe and Steve Zeitlin. Reprinted by permission of Henry Holt and Company, LLC.

"Theo and Rustbucket" by Douglas Holgate.

Reprinted with the permission of Simon Spotlight entertainment, an imprint of Simon & Schuster Children's Publishing Division, from *The Story of My Life: An Afghan Girl on the Other Side of the Sky* by Farah Ahmedi with Tamim Ansary. Text copyright © 2005 Nestegg Productions LLC.

"Mother Doesn't Want a Dog" by Judith Viorst, reprinted with the permission of Atheneum Books for Young Readers, an imprint of Simon & Schuster Children's Publishing Division, from *If I Were in Charge of the World and Other Worries* by Judith Viorst. Text copyright © 1981 by Judith Viorst.

"Merry-Go-Round: Colored Child at Carnival" from *Selected Poems of Langston Hughes* by Langston Hughes, copyright © 1927 by Alfred A. Knopf Inc. and renewed 1955 by Langston Hughes. Used by permission of Alfred A. Knopf, a division of Random House, Inc.

"Cheating: Excuses, Excuses" It's My Life (ages 8-13) www.pbskids.org/itsmylife/ school. In the Mix ages (13-18), www. inthemix.org Episode #604: Ethics: Cheating and Plagiarism. Reprinted by permission of Castle Works.

Acknowledgments

"What a Wish!" from *Girls' Life*, December 2005. Reprinted by permission of *Girls' Life* magazine.

Unit 4

"Los Lonely Boys Sound Off" by Ron Arias, published in *People*, July 26, 2004. Copyright © 2004 by Time, Inc. Reprinted by permission.

"Pig Brains" by Alden R. Carter. Reprinted by permission of the author.

"Amazing Animals: Beavers Busted" by Deborah Underwood, from *NationalGeographicKids.com*. Reprinted by permission of the National Geographic Society.

"My Self Myself" from *Finding Our Way* by René Saldaña, Jr., copyright © 2003 by René Saldaña, Jr. Used by permission of Random House Children's Books, a division of Random House, Inc.

From *The Blues Singers* by Julius Lester. Copyright © 2001 by Julius Lester. Reprinted by Hyperion Books for Children.

From "Behind the Scenes of…*High School Musical*" by Gerri Miller. Published in *Scholastic News*, February 6, 2006. Copyright © 2006 by Scholastic Inc. Reprinted by permission.

"Alienation!" by Steven Maxwell.

Excerpt from "The Whole World in His Hands" from *The Way a Door Closes* by Hope Anita Smith. Copyright © 2003 by Hope Anita Smith. Reprinted by permission of Henry Holt and Company, LLC.

"Epiphany" by Ellen Wittlinger. Copyright © Ellen Wittlinger, 2004. Reprinted by permission of Curtis Brown, Ltd.

"Mama's Magic" by Glenis Redmond, from *Poetry Slam: The Competitive Art of Performance Poetry*, copyright © 2000 Manic D Press. Reprinted by permission. All rights reserved.

Glencoe would like to acknowledge the artists who participated in illustrating this program: Bizet Kizcorn; Jerzy Drozd and Sara Turner; Douglas Holgate; and Steven Maxwell.

Photo credits

Getty Images; **148** CORBIS; **149** Image100 Ltd.; **150** Michael Kevin Daly/CORBIS; **151** (t)CORBIS, (b)FogStock/Index Open; **152** FogStock/IndexOpen; **153** Geoff Manasse/Getty Images; **154** C Squared Studios/Getty Images; **155** Digital Vision Ltd./Getty Images; **156** Xavier Bonghi/Getty Images; **157** McGraw-Hill Companies; **158** Jonnie Miles/Getty Images; **159** Digital Vision/PunchStock; **160** BananaStock/2006 JupiterImages Corporation; **161** Getty Images; **163** Francis Miller/Time Life Pictures/Getty Images; **164** MPI/Getty Images; **167** 2006 JupiterImages Corporation/photos.com; **168** Siede Preis/Getty Images; **170** 2006 JupiterImages Corporation/photos.com; **183** Krisanne Johnson/White House via Getty Images; **186** Reuters/CORBIS; **191** David Buffington/Getty Images; **193** Richard Lewisohn/Digital Vision/Getty Images; **196** Image100 Ltd.; **198** (inset)Dynamic Graphics/2006 JupiterImages Corporation, (bkgd)Masterfile; **202** Digital Vision/PunchStock; **204** Brand X Pictures/PunchStock; **206** Jakub Mosur/AP/Wide World Photos; **207** Brand X Pictures/PunchStock; **208** (t)Nick Koudis/Getty Images, (b)Image Source/PunchStock; **213** Francis Hammond/Getty Images; **215** Allan Rosenberg/Cole Group/Getty Images; **217** Dougal Waters/Getty Images; **219** 2006 JupiterImages Corporation/photos.com; **220** Creatas/PunchStock; **224** Digital Vision/PunchStock; **227** Brad Goodell/Getty Images; **229** Getty Images; **231** AP/Wide World Photos; **233** Mark J. Terrill/AP/Wide World Photos; **235** Richard Drew/AP/Wide World Photos; **236** Jennifer Graylock/AP/Wide World Photos; **238** (l)CORBIS, (r)Richard Drew/AP/Wide World Photos; **251** (inset)CORBIS, (bkgd)CORBIS; **253 257** (l)Getty Images, (r)Getty Images; **261** CORBIS; **262** AbleStock/Index Open; **264** CORBIS; **266 267** Hot Ideas/Index Open; **268** SW Productions/Getty Images; **273** (inset)Getty Images, (bkgd)Dynamic Graphics/2006 JupiterImages Corporation; **273** (bkgd)Todd Boroson (NOAO), AURA, NOAO, NSF.